HORIZONS

HORIZONS

NORMAN BEL GEDDES

Boston · LITTLE, BROWN, AND COMPANY · 1932

COPYRIGHT, 1932, BY NORMAN BEL GEDDES

PRINTED IN THE UNITED STATES OF AMERICA

CONTENTS

ILLUSTRATIONS

HORIZONS

IN INDUSTRIAL DESIGN

CHAPTER I

Towards Design

We enter a new era. Are we ready for the changes that are coming? The houses we live in to-morrow will not much resemble the houses we live in to-day. Automobiles, railway trains, theaters, cities, industry itself, are undergoing rapid changes. Likewise, art in all its forms. The forms they presently take will undoubtedly have kinship with the forms we know in the present; but this relationship will be as distinct, and probably as remote, as that between the horseless buggy of yesterday and the present-day motor car.

We live and work under pressure with a tremendous expenditure of energy. We feel that life in our time is more urgent, complex and discordant than life ever was before. That may be so. In the perspective of fifty years hence, the historian will detect in the decade of 1930-1940 a period of tremendous significance. He will see it as a period of criticism, unrest, and dissatisfaction to the point of disillusion — when new aims were being sought and new beginnings were astir. Doubtless he will ponder that, in the midst of a world-wide melancholy owing to an economic depression, a new age dawned with invigorating conceptions and the horizon lifted.

Critics of the age are agreed upon one thought: that what industry has given us, as yet, is not good enough. Another plea of critics hostile to the age is that machines make automatons of men. They fail to see that the machine age is not really here. Although we built the machines, we have not become at ease with them and have not mastered them. Our condition is the result of a swift industrial evolution. If we see the situation clearly, we realize that we have been infatuated with our own mechanical ingenuity. Rapidly multiplying our products, creating and glorifying the gadget, we have been inferior craftsmen, the victims rather than the masters of our ingenuity. In our evolution we have accumulated noise, dirt, glitter, speed, mass production, traffic congestion, and the commonplace by our machine-made ideas. But that is only one side.

We have achieved the beginnings of an expression of our time. We now have some inkling of what to-day's home, to-day's theater, to-day's factory, to-day's city, should be. We perceive that the person who would use a machine must be imbued with the spirit of the machine and comprehend the nature of his materials. We realize that he is creating the telltale environment that records what man truly is.

It happens that the United States has seized upon more of the fruits of industrialism than any other nation. We have gone farther and more swiftly than any other. To what end? Not the least tendency is the searching and brooding uncertainty, the quest for basic truths which characterize the present day. Never before, in an economic crisis, has there been such an aroused consciousness on the part of the community at large and within industry itself. Complacency has vanished. A new horizon appears. A horizon that will inspire the next phase in the evolution of the age.

We are entering an era which, notably, shall be characterized by *design* in four specific phases: Design in social structure to insure the organization of people, work, wealth, leisure. Design in machines that shall improve working conditions by eliminating drudgery. Design in all objects of daily use that shall make them economical, durable, convenient, congenial to every one. Design in the arts, painting, sculpture, music, literature, and architecture, that shall inspire the new era.

The impetus towards design in industrial life to-day must be considered from three viewpoints: the consumer's, the manufacturer's, and the artist's. In his appreciation of the importance of design the artist is somewhat ahead of the consumer, while the average manufacturer is farther behind the consumer than the consumer is behind the artist. The viewpoint of each is rapidly changing, developing, fusing. More than that, the economic situation is stimulating a unanimity of emphasis, a merger of viewpoints.

Until recently artists have been disposed to isolate themselves upon the side of life apart from business; apart from a changing world which, in their opinion, was less sympathetic because its output, in becoming machine-made, was losing its individuality. The few artists who have devoted themselves to industrial design have done so with condescension, regarding it as a surrender to Mammon, a mere source of income to enable them to obtain time for creative work. On the other hand, I was drawn to industry by the great opportunities it offered *creatively*.

For years I had thought of these possibilities and hesitated only due to the years I had put into the theater. In 1927, I decided that I would no longer devote myself exclusively to the theater, but would experiment in designing motor cars, ships, factories, railways — sources more vitally akin to life to-day than the theater. The theater of the present moment is marking time due to the tremendous progress of talking pictures. Many of my friends interpreted my decision as an eccentric gesture and predicted that my new venture would be short-lived. Actually this change represented no violent

[5]

jump from the identically sincere principles upon which I had always worked. It was a natural evolution. What amazes me is that more men have not done the same thing.

An artist is sensitive to his environment. As you look back and think of Egypt, [Plate 1] of Greece,[2] of any of the outstanding eras in the past, you visualize the culture and environment as something to which the artist was susceptible. More than that, he played the important part in creating what you visualize as that era. When working in the theater, it was my endeavor to handle my materials in terms of my own time rather than that of my grandparents. As a matter of fact, I have felt a sense of duty about it. I have felt, and still feel, that it is primarily laziness and a lack of courage on the part of many of my colleague designers in the theater that they fail to do so. In view of this, nothing could be more natural than the step I took. Whether you are sympathetic to the idea or not, industry is the driving force of this age. One of my dearest friends thinks it is the ruination of the age; that we would all be much better if our only possessions were breechcloths and if our homes were a peak in the Himalayas. He may be right. Even that fails to alter conditions that *are*.

1 · TEMPLE OF AMON, LUXOR   DESIGNER UNKNOWN 1450 B. C.

Ewing Galloway

Standards of art are changing as rapidly as standards of wealth and government. Past generations have looked at statues erected on corners and parkways;[3] future generations will make monuments of a different caliber. Due to its stark simplicity, one of the few memorials of the last century that will withstand changes in thought and time is the Washington Monument.[4] I foresee art being released from its picture frames and prosceniums and pedestals and museums and bursting forth in more inspired forms. I firmly believe that the statue on its pedestal and the painting in its frame will eventually vanish as mediums of expression. Art in the coming generations will have less and less to do with frames, pedestals, museums, books and concert halls and more to do with people and their life.

In the point of view of the artist who fails to see an æsthetic appeal in such objects of contemporary life as a railway train,[55] a suspension bridge,[178] a grain elevator,[17] a dynamo,[16] there is an inconsistency. Would that same artist put an apple or a flower in a bowl, make a careful painting of it, and think that he has created a work of art? Is it the subject matter, his technical limitations, or his lack of imagination? Charcoal, paint and clay, to be

2 · PARTHENON   DESIGNED BY ICTINUS & CALLICRATES 447 B. C.

Ewing Galloway

3 · CIVIC VIRTUE MONUMENT
DESIGNED BY FREDERICK MacMONNIES 1922

sure, are much more sensitive to the subtleties of individual expression than sheet metal, in the same sense that the violin and the piano offer virtuoso possibilities beyond the oboe or trumpet. On the other hand, steamships, airplanes, and radios present the same organic problems in terms of design as do architecture, sculpture, and literature. Keats wrote a few immortal lines about a Grecian urn. Had he known about it and felt like it, he could have written them about an airplane.

Whether or not a man is an artist is determined solely by his work. His private life, the money he earns, his philosophy, his vices, are all beside the point. I know personally most of the serious artists in America and a good number abroad. Regardless of what their mediums are, whether they are painters, sculptors, musicians or poets, they are as much concerned about the money they earn as any average person, including the typical "commercial artist." However, there is one outstanding difference between them. The commercial artist does what he does with dollars as his inspiration, while the other fellow, *the* artist, does what he does with the work itself as inspiration. El Greco might have been a magazine illustrator or a bricklayer, but he still would have been a great artist. Cézanne' at an early stage of his career designed candy-box covers. His widow once very kindly showed them to me in his own house. Gauguin was a banker until he was forty years old.

The general public's idea of artists is derived from the assortment of people who pass by that title. Furthermore the public labors under two handicaps in its judgment of artists. One is that the work of artists is intriguing and mysterious. And any one possessing the barest fundamentals of a technical knowledge on the subject feels himself to be beyond the comprehension of the general public. The other is a belief on the part of most people that they are competent to criticize art, although the same person would be much more modest regarding a scientific problem. In our world of to-day Picasso, an artist, bears the same importance to our life as Einstein, a scientist. In the case of Picasso, the average intelligent person does not understand his work nor does he accept it.' Einstein is accepted as a matter of course. There is no question in the mind of any one who knows about art that Picasso is one of the greatest painters that has ever lived. The fact that he is forward-looking and experimental gives the same significance to his work as is the case with Einstein. This same general public does not realize that the works of artists whom they now accept — as Corot,' Millet, and Turner — were, in their day, regarded as the works of Picasso are at the present moment. Further than that, they do not know that Picasso has already exerted more influence on the works of future artists than the other three men combined.

There are probably more misconceptions about artists than about any other people. Inspiration is a great asset not only to artists but to any one else. Nevertheless there are many people who think an artist lives on it. I have one client who on numerous occasions has expressed the keenest disappointment at my never having come into his office unexpectedly and exclaimed wildly about some idea that I got the

[9]

5 · SEATED WOMAN   PAINTING BY PABLO PICASSO 1929

night before as a result of being inebriated. A grown man, a very successful nationally known business man, he looks upon the artist with the same perplexed admiration that the small boy bestows upon the vaudeville magician.

The work of the artist always has been, and will be, a distinctly individual product — the antithesis of "machine-made." Fundamentally, the artist is an emotional person in that he relies more upon his feelings and intuitions than upon reasoning. His reaction against the machine, even though it may duplicate a work of his with an exactness beyond his own capabilities and beyond any criticism he can make of it, is an intuitive one. Years ago, when I saw a well-known sculptor using a pneumatic drill to cut away the rough elements from

Metropolitan Museum

6 · SOUVENIR de MORTEFONTAINE   PAINTING BY JEAN B. C. COROT 1846

a statue he was working on, my estimate of him took a sudden drop. I was young and I did not know that to-day's sculptors use such implements. That he was not chipping away with a mallet and chisel was a disillusion that I failed to get over for a long time. The reaction was instinctive and natural.

During the Renaissance, statues, tombs, and churches were the industry of the times. Michelangelo loved sculpture and detested painting.[7] He painted for purely mercenary reasons. When he decorated the ceiling of the Sistine Chapel he was turning out the great moving-picture epic of his day. The eighteenth-century painter put fruit on a table, made a painstaking copy of it, and in proportion to its realism, it was acclaimed a work of art.[8]

7 · MOSES FROM THE TOMB OF POPE JULIUS DESIGNED BY MICHELANGELO 1513

Cézanne made his point emphatically and for all time that the subject matter bears no relation to a work of art.[9] It is this same point of view that has caused to-day's artist to break from the old standards and caused him to realize that the machines have created problems he alone can solve. Sensitive to color and form, he has begun to see inspiring possibilities in these problems that industry has created but cannot solve without him.

How or by what means an artist expresses himself is of no consequence. It is the vitality and subtlety of feeling which results that gives the work its place in the sun, and it makes no difference whether it was achieved with paint, stone or machine. Camera still life illustrates emphatically that interest in visual form is not the result of subject matter.[10] Neither can technical dexterity alone accomplish the result. An artist always, eventually, acquires expert-

[12]

ness, but that is not what made him an artist. Has it ever occurred to you that a photograph of a flower, even though devoid of color, might be as thrilling as a painting of it,[11] or that six plow blades, laid side by side and photographed would form a striking pat-

8 · STILL LIFE

PAINTING BY EMILIE PREYER 1849

tern?[12] Or that, in the hands of an artist, eight pairs of spectacles could win your æsthetic admiration?[13]

So much for the artist's viewpoint. Let us consider the consumer. The consumer has seen and read advertisements and has turned trustingly to industry. But industry, with some conspicuous exceptions, has failed him. It has forced consumers to buy below their taste. Sales organizations have educated the

mass to accept the mediocre as criterion, offering at a reasonable price, not genuine creations, but spurious substitutes of a mongrel-imitation-period type.[189] Do not misunderstand me; the in-

9 · STILL LIFE

PAINTING BY PAUL CEZANNE 1895

10 · STILL LIFE   PHOTOGRAPH BY RALPH STEINER 1930

tent of the manufacturers was not this — just their lack of good taste to the point of basing their business on it. Even so and despite all such education, the viewpoint of the mass continues to improve. Some people think of mass action as a thing of our lifetime — of labor unions and the like — forgetting that this country was founded by mass action; forgetting endless historical instances; within our own generation this change probably began with such matters as hours worked per week, and payment per hour, and conveniences and comforts of everyday life such as more " fortunate " people have. Mass desires to-day go beyond shorter hours. Higher wages are related to aspirations for better living. As a natural result, they are acquiring a taste that is different from that fostered by the master merchandisers for their consumption. The mass to-day is not interested in mere living but in living the way they would *like* to live.

Mass production was welcomed as a means of raising the standard of everyday life. In the beginning, it was taken for granted that in cheap machine products satisfactory working results were the most that could be expected. More recently, since mass production has attained new standards of practica-

[14]

bility, and durability, and cheapness of process, a new attitude on the part of the consumer has made itself felt most emphatically. "Durable and cheap, but look at it!"[184] is the result of an inherent belief that the object which looks good may be expected to have other good qualities!

In what happened several years ago to Mr. Ford's Model T, the famous and ugly forerunner of his better-looking models of the present day, we have an example of the manner in which consumer demand forced a manufacturer to become aware of the existence of public taste. An attractive car took the place of Model T forced by competition. This competition had long been latent. No competitor could have created it merely as a weapon of trade. It

II · STILL LIFE   PHOTOGRAPH BY IMOGEN CUNNINGHAM 1925

[15]

vas a tidal force, the real, though inarticulate demand on the part of the people for quality of appearance. A clinical chart would have shown an improvement in the national blood pressure with the disappearance of Model T!

The average manufacturer, instead of offering the public a straightforward, sincerely designed product, frankly made of whatever material is most suited to its manufacture, frequently distrusts the market. For instance, radio manufacturers feel compelled to produce imitation period furniture.[189] There is no justification for not designing a small piece of furniture, such as the radio, at least as simply as the average grand piano ten times its bulk. Manufacturers and merchants, however, insist that they must dress up the radio because of its mechanical aspect — that the public dislikes any suggestion of its functional qualities. Why, then, does not the public object to most of the clocks on the market? Why isn't the telephone camouflaged to look like a Grecian urn?

This attitude is not true of all manufacturers, of course. There are conspicuous exceptions. In my experience since entering this field I have been tremendously impressed by the enthusiastic interest and response of manufacturers and merchandisers. Their attitude has been, to a great extent, one of surprise that an artist of standing showed any interest in what they were doing; and they have shown both surprise and delight upon finding that it is possible for an artist to work in terms identical with those to which they are accustomed. And now, for reasons that are obvious, we may anticipate that the attitude of the exceptionally far-sighted manufacturer of to-day will be the attitude of the average manufacturer of to-morrow. The successful industrialist with a blind spot for design will presently be a rarity. The facts of the economic situation point in this direction.

Yesterday's merchandising psychology was to follow in the wake of popular demand and to supply it. To-morrow's merchandising policy must necessarily be to anticipate public demand and supply it. Since public demand now is for quality in appearance as well as for quality in service, artists and industry will still further unite their efforts to win the confidence of the public. How, you may ask, will design in the future differ from design in the past? Let me preface my answer to the question by explaining briefly what design means to me.

A design is a mental conception of something to be done. A visual design is the organism of an idea of a visual nature so that it may be executed. It is the practice of organizing various elements to produce a desired result. Design deals exclusively with organization and arrangement of form. It is the opposite of accidental. It is deliberate thinking, planning to a purpose.

12 · PLOW BLADES
PHOTOGRAPH BY MARGARET BOURKE-WHITE 1929

The objective of an industrial designer is not different from the objective of any other designer. A designer is a designer for about the same reasons that a business man (if he is a good one) is a business man: because his major inclinations flow in that direction. His aptitudes, education, experience, knowledge, and desires are an integral part of him, and point to design. No matter

13 · SPECTACLES
PHOTOGRAPH BY EDWARD STEICHEN 1929

what he does, in work or play, in one location or another, he thinks in terms of design. It is natural to him. He is intrigued with the materials of his medium, their advantages and limitations and the possibilities of expression they offer.

In order to discuss design, a distinction must

[17]

Stehli Silk Corporation

be made between surface qualities and structural qualities. Nevertheless, surface qualities and structural qualities should not be treated separately. The former must be the direct expression of the latter, otherwise there is a lack of sincerity and vitality in the total unit.

Organic surface qualities are the direct expression of the functional requirements of the problem. An unorganic surface treatment is a mere ornamental dress. The Gothic adornment of the Woolworth Building, for instance, is applied decoration in contrast with the straightforward treatment of the News Building by Raymond Hood. Or, compare Benvenuto Cellini's famous but despicable design for a cup[14] with the cylix of an unknown Greek designer.[15]

Visual design is concerned with form, space, color; with the proportioning of solids and voids and the rhythmic spacings of these elements. The governing factor as to what is pleasing to the eye is the *idea*, which is of an emotional nature — an emotion of pleasure, satisfaction, excitement, exhilaration, stimulation. This reaction varies with the character

14 · ROSPIGLIOSI CUP
DESIGNED BY BENVENUTO CELLINI 1560

Metropolitan Museum

and quality of the idea. Originality and inspiration are two necessary requirements for advanced work in the field of design. They must take root from the conditions and functions of the problem involved. In the Parthenon, for instance, you can find no detail of a superfluous nature.[2] This is the result of perfect design.

Our early architects, whom we speak of as " Colonial," built their houses,

[18]

barns, windmills and furniture with the same spirit and with the same fine quality that appears in the structures of the ancient Greeks. But the Colonials had a distinctly different combination of materials with which to work."[8] The result they achieved was a sincere, direct expression of the requirements of their problem. Its best examples are simple, honest and fine.

Such perfection is yet to be achieved in our skyscraper form of architecture. In the skyscraper the basic elements are the steel frame and the material enclosing this frame. Until now, this material has been a solid composed of brick or concrete or stone in combination with glass. Ornament, in such forms as decorative cornices, horizontal bands, part of them way up the structure and more along the base, has been considered necessary as a relief to the eye. Architects, having been schooled in materials and principles permitting of such views and consequently believing in them, will tell you that the public would be unhappy if such ornamentation were not employed. Designers of automobiles, who have not been able to free themselves from the precedent of the horseless carriage or coach, take much the same view in their work. How out of place the moldings and gadgets that we see on our automobile, even of the smartest type, would appear if we saw them on an airplane! When the airplane was developed, it was an all new problem. Its requirements were such that it never occurred to any one to base its design principles on, for instance, a carriage with wings.

15 · GREEK CYLIX

DESIGNER UNKNOWN 550 B. C.

Metropolitan Museum

One may say that when the design of an object is in keeping with the purpose it serves, it appeals to us as having a distinctive kind of beauty. That is why we are impressed by the stirring beauty of airplanes.[19] The underlying principle of the emotional response that the airplane stirs in us would seem to be the same as that which accounts for the emotional effect of the finest architecture — the form, proportion, and color best suited to that object's purpose. To arrive at the most satisfactory form for any object, the purpose it is to fulfill and the intuition and intelligence of the designer must fuse. The subject makes but slight difference. Of course the designer must study and understand the subject in order to interpret it. He must have a thorough knowledge of the purpose the subject is to fulfill and the simplest means of bringing this about. If he is an artist, as well as a designer, he will accomplish this in a way that will arouse an unusual amount of interest in the onlooker. This latter is the expression of his individuality and it is this particular item that is his greatest asset.

When Rembrandt painted a model, friend or stranger, the significance of his picture did not depend upon his subject, but upon the painter's ability to put on his canvas something of the interest he felt in the subject and in such a manner that it creates a profound emotional response in the majority of people looking at it. To-day we do not know that as portraits they were even likenesses — nor do we care. We do know they are works of art. It is much the same with any other form of creative work. When Wagner composed The Ring he was so absorbed by the emotional excitement of the idea that he put into his music an undefinable rhythmic and melodic combination that stirs any one who hears it. The same can be said of a popular tune, but its span of life is shorter.

The qualities that account for the appeal in experiencing a painting by Manet, a score by Beethoven, the Great Pyramid, Pavlova's dancing, Shakespeare's writing, those qualities which invade the subconscious, stir us deeply, linger in the memory, can only be defined as emotional. The qualities that make one steamship, vase, airplane, or skyscraper appeal to us, while another does not, are of the same nature. When we look at a painting that pleases us, we experience a definite emotional reaction. It may be subdued or even subconscious. Any one who enjoys Da Vinci's painting of the Mona Lisa in the Louvre experiences such an emotion. The same is true with reference to Rodin's Burghers of Calais, or a tale of Poe's. When we listen to music that we enjoy, it is an emotional experience. When this emotion disappears we begin to be bored.

When viewing a scene which strikes you as beautiful, you experience an emotion. When you stand on a hill along the Monongahela River, looking out over miles

Margaret Bourke-White

16 · DYNAMOS NIAGARA HUDSON POWER PLANT
DESIGNER UNKNOWN

of steel mills, hundreds of stacks belching flame, you are experiencing an emotion. You may have had the same experience in a château in France, in the Metropolitan Museum of Art, on the rim of the Grand Canyon, or when looking at a piece of furniture, or even at a fragile wineglass. Likewise, if the sight of the Akron or of Man o' War leading the field down the home stretch excites you, you are reacting to an emotion. When automobiles, railway cars,

[21]

Margaret Bourke-White

DESIGNED BY JAMES METCALF 19

airships, steamships or other objects of an industrial nature stimulate you in the same way that you are stimulated when you look at the Parthenon, at the windows of Chartres, at the Moses of Michelangelo, or at the frescos of Giotto, you will then have every right to speak of them as works of art.

Just as surely as the artists of the fourteenth century are remembered by their cathedrals, so will those of the twentieth be remembered for their factories and the products of these factories.

CHAPTER 2

Speed — To-morrow

THE development of mechanical transportation began a little more than one hundred years ago. To-day, speed is the cry of our era, and greater speed one of the goals of to-morrow.

Giving vent to the contemporary fear of terrific speed, the *Quarterly Review*, in 1825, exclaimed: " What can be more palpably absurd than the prospect held out of locomotives travelling twice as fast as stagecoaches? " And stagecoach operators of Great Britain were elated when " experts " declared that the railroad would be useless for human transport because man could not endure speeds of from twenty to thirty miles an hour to which speed maniacs proposed to subject them!

With developments in the realm of speed during the intervening century, we are all more or less familiar. With every advance, sceptics have not been wanting. Scepticism greeted the spluttering, stuttering, one-lunged buggy-automobile in the early days of Ford. It was the prelude to the performance of the Wrights at Kitty Hawk.[85] And always, speculators who have sold short developments in the realm of speed have found themselves worse confounded.

Year after year, speed records have been broken. Ultimate limitations on speed have now been pushed so far beyond the horizon that sceptics are silent. Optimism rules. One hears the easy, offhand prediction that the motor car will attain five hundred and the airplane a thousand miles an hour, as though this were a matter of course!

Speed, we say, is the direct result of power. Hence the uninformed optimist may conclude that we have only to put greater engines in the car or in the airplane in order to attain greater speed. But the problem is far more complex and varied, requiring the combined efforts of the engineer, the chemist, the designer; and one of them, at least, must possess great imagination. Exactly what I mean by this will appear if we consider some possible trends in the future design of motor cars, airplanes, locomotives and steamships.

Within the speed range of the automobile or the railroad train, an increase in speed of the vehicle produces an increased air resistance proportional to the square of the speed; also, the power required to increase the speed must be increased as its cube. Where such large amounts of power are required to produce relatively small increases in speed, it becomes imperative that all factors tending to produce resistance be minimized. Conversely the elimination of resistance-creating factors permits the same power plant to produce greater speeds, or to operate more efficiently at lower speeds. The present-day motor car of conventional design offers about five times the resistance of a perfectly streamlined vehicle. We realize at once that the efficiency of the design is a factor definitely controlling the higher speeds we anticipate for to-morrow.

Captain Sir Malcolm Campbell established a record of 245.733 miles per hour at Daytona Beach — over two miles a minute faster than the average airplane flies, but two miles a minute slower than the fastest airplane had flown till then. On the basis of computations by Helmholtz, this is twice as fast as the time required for man to coördinate brain and hand. At such speed, objects seen in passing do not enter the consciousness until the driver is many yards past them. Obviously, we must assume that there is a definite limit to the speed at which the human hand can guide a car. Experiment alone can tell. At the moment we may assume that this limit lies somewhere in the neighborhood of three hundred miles an hour.

To-morrow, engineering science (and all the sciences allied with it for the production of requisite materials) will undoubtedly be equal to solving the enormous problems involved in producing a car equal to a speed of three hundred miles an hour. The problems are formidable, but not insuperable. They involve the power plant, refinements in structure and design, and other equally important considerations concerning thermo-efficiency, the resistance of fabrics to centrifugal force, and the strength of materials.

In the development of transportation and speed we have reached that point where *design* is increasingly important from the viewpoint of efficiency and safety. The nature of some of these design problems is brought out in high relief in the light of certain features of the Blue Bird in which Campbell established his record.[18] Many things which affect an ordinary automobile only incidentally affect tremendously a high speed car such as the Blue Bird. When making four miles a minute, it has to combat a relative wind speed of two hundred and forty miles an hour. While enormous pressure is thus exerted upon the front of the car, the back of the car is ordinarily in a partial vacuum. The result is what engineers describe as negative pressure. If the condition is sufficiently marked, the car tends to turn turtle.

Distribution of the relative wind pressure as evenly as possible fore and aft

Keystone View

must be accomplished by the most careful streamlining. The wheels themselves are streamlined. The effect streamlining has upon any object moving through a fluid, such as air or water, is tremendous." Fairing is placed behind the front wheels to reduce the eddies and keep the air as free as possible from turbulence. Since the air which meets the rear wheels is turbulent to a degree, the fairing is placed at both front and rear.

Designing the wheels for a machine capable of such speed is in itself a tremendous problem. When a solid steel flywheel revolves beyond what is known as its critical speed, it flies to pieces, owing to the centrifugal force. When the Blue Bird attained a speed of two hundred and forty-five miles an hour, its wheels made in the neighborhood of twenty-three hundred revolutions a minute. At this speed the ordinary tire tread would be thrown off in tatters. In consequence, the tires were treadless. We are able to comprehend the effect of the centrifugal force from the fact that, when at rest, the wheels of the Blue Bird have a radius of seventeen and a half inches. At one hundred and fifty miles per hour, the radius increases to nineteen inches.

The Blue Bird is equipped with a supercharged airplane engine, a fourteen hundred horse-power Napier. Direct transmission from engine to the rear axle was impossible for the reason that this would have pushed the driver up to such a height that his presence would have interfered with the streamlining. By an indirect drive, the transmission shaft being offset to the left of center, this difficulty was overcome. The driver's head is only thirty-nine and a half inches above the ground.

One of the interesting features in the design of this particular machine is the large vertical fin at the rear of the car. Its function is to serve as a stabilizer, without which it would have been impossible to keep the car moving in a straight line. At high racing speeds the slightest swerve is accompanied by possibly critical consequences. A change of direction on the part of a car

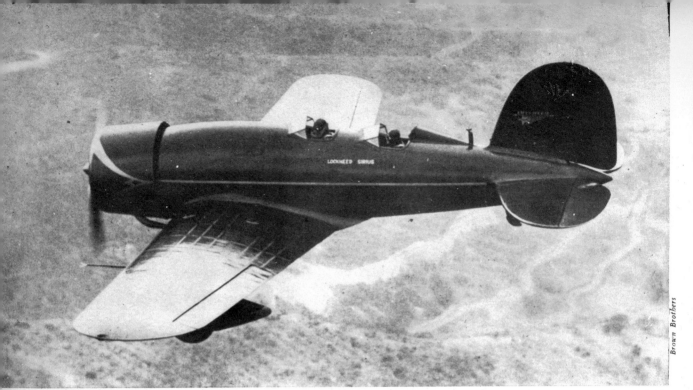

Brown Brothers

19 · LOCKHEED SIRIUS PLANE   DESIGNED BY JOHN K. NORTHROP, RICHARD VON HAKE, ALLAN LOCGHEAD, GERALD VULTEE 1929

speeding at two hundred and forty-five miles an hour causes the air pressure to be increased on one side and decreased on the other. The presence of the fin tends to keep the car in its original line of motion.

Numerous problems having to do with velocity remain to be solved, even when the car has once been effectively streamlined. Owing to inertia, water, fuel and air are pressed sharply against the rear of their containers. This inertia is sufficient to offset the force of gravity. While, ordinarily, the gas tank in the Blue Bird would have been a gravity tank, in view of its position, the effect of the inertia had to be overcome by a powerful automatic pressure pump in order to make certain a free and adequate flow of gas to the carburetors.

In a car going at two hundred and forty-five miles an hour the driver finds it impossible to put the brakes on suddenly. His strength is not adequate. If he had enough strength and did apply the brakes suddenly, the drums would instantly burn out, owing to the friction. Hence, in order to bring the machine to a stop, it is necessary first to let the momentum diminish. Then the driver presses a pedal which connects with a vacuum motor. This motor puts the brakes on more evenly than the ablest driver.

The plane in which Lieutenant Stainforth, at Calshot, following the Schneider trophy contest, September, 1931, gained the world speed record of 415.2 miles an hour, was equipped with a Rolls-Royce 2560 horse-power engine consuming over 2 gallons of fuel a minute. Compare this with the spluttering 16 horse-power motor of 1903. A roaring 2500 horse-power engine taxes the resources of the designer. The waste heat developed is enough to generate 1000 horse-power per minute. What shall be done with it? Radiator pipes must be spread out so as not to spoil the streamline contour. There is danger of premature firing because of the temperatures to which cylinder walls are heated. Where is the metallurgical chemist who will present us with new alloys that can withstand such intense heat?

It has been predicted that very soon we shall be traveling through the air at anywhere from seven hundred and fifty to a thousand miles an hour. Such predictions are the result of extreme and possibly unfounded optimism. With our limited knowledge of aeronautics, one may well hesitate to predict the ultimate speed of the air-plane.

20 · ZEPPELIN RAIL CAR
DESIGNED BY FRANZ KRUCKENBERG & CURT STEDEFELD 1929

To-day, the average speed of express transport air-planes falls considerably be-low three hundred miles an hour. However, the day will come when for ordinary commercial purposes an air-plane speed of three hun-dred miles an hour will be

Keystone View

practicable. Some believe that this is the ultimate speed of airplanes for ordinary commercial purposes. We are justified in foreseeing that for military purposes airplanes will attain five hundred miles an hour. Flights at such speeds will presumably always have certain elements of risk.

When engineers, not to-morrow, but at some time in the not too remote future, succeed in building an airplane that can fly one thousand miles an

Brown Brothers

hour, will the thousand-mile-an-hour plane be guided by a human pilot in the plane itself or by an automatic pilot and controlled from the ground by wireless? The question would be simpler to answer if we could be sure of gradually increasing the speed at a rate no greater than the acceleration of gravity; and if we could be sure of never stopping suddenly, and of never interrupting the momentum by a sharp turn or by a sudden, though slight rise or descent in flight. When suddenly applying the brakes of your automobile while traveling at forty miles an hour, you may have been thrown forward over the wheel. When starting suddenly, you have been jerked backward against the seat cushions. Magnify that experience hundreds of times and you find it not difficult to imagine the result that would follow from a sharp break in the momentum of the plane traveling at a thousand miles an hour.

Of one thing I am positive. The airship of the future, regardless of its kind, will be as fool-proof as an automobile. I have no idea as to how it will be achieved, but I am positive that it will be. Many more remarkable things than this have been accomplished. With our flying at the present moment, we are in the position of a boy who, having jumped off the end of a dock without knowing the principles of swimming, is barely able to keep himself afloat. He kicks and splashes about and manages to stay on top. Nevertheless, he could not do it for long, nor in a choppy sea. On the other hand, once he has mastered a few simple principles, he finds that, after all, swimming is not so difficult.

A robot, built on the lines of the gyroscope, or on some principle yet to be discovered, may ultimately overcome for aviation the problem now present in the human factor. However, the extent to which it can be worked out to control the ship through various flying conditions, automatically offsetting unforeseen situations and complications such as running into other ships in the air, in landing and reacting properly to air-traffic regulations, is so far beyond the present status of aircraft development problems that it is mere speculation to comment upon the ultimate possibilities.

The future of the railroad is a problem regarding which engineering science is in a quandary. My own opinion is that further development as regards locomotives and trains will have to do with comfort, efficiency, and safety rather than with an appreciable increase in speed. For a long-distance locomotive run the record is 102.3 miles per hour between Plymouth and London. That record has stood since 1904.

During the opening years of the present century, the competition between the railroads engendered a battle for speed. When the New York Central announced an eighteen-hour train from New York to Chicago, the Pennsylvania Railroad, though it had to climb the Alleghenies, as against the level route of the New York Central, retaliated by the announcement of another eighteen-hour train. When the Central cut the time to seventeen hours, the Pennsylvania did likewise. Thereupon, the Central put into effect a schedule requiring its express to cover the distance of nine hundred and ninety-one miles in sixteen hours — an average speed, including stops, of sixty-two miles an hour. Thundering around a curve at a little too much speed, a train sheared off the rail spikes and went over an embankment, though without loss of life. This was the end of the competition for speed. Until recently, the New York Central and the Pennsylvania have held to a twenty-hour schedule for their best trains. Twelve hours between New York and Chicago by train is not impossible but neither is it justified economically in the light of present-day progress in aviation, where even greater speeds are practical at considerably less cost.

Engineers could unquestionably design a locomotive equal to a speed greater than that at which any locomotive has ever been driven. Perhaps they would use steam; perhaps not. The really vital problems have to do with other

22 · S. S. BREMEN   DESIGNED BY DEUTSCHE SHIFF & MASCHINENBAU A. G., WERK A. G. WESER 1928

North German Lloyd

factors, such as the design of the rolling equipment and the maintenance of the roadbed. Certainly, in view of changing conditions, we may expect the railroads eventually to attain far better sustained speeds than are now possible. European experiments with regard to high-speed automotive units, designed for steel rails, point that way. A hundred miles an hour is not an impossible goal under certain conditions where traffic warrants it. Railroad men predict that, twenty years hence, short-unit trains of the automotive type, capable of a hundred miles an hour, may be dispatched every ten or fifteen minutes from New York to Boston, to Buffalo, and to Washington.

In Germany, there is now in use a propeller-drive car running on a stretch of ordinary railroad track.[20] It has reached a speed of 113 miles per hour, and the indications are that a much greater velocity can be attained over long distances. This new "zeppelin on rails" resembles a low streamlined railway coach. The frame is slung between the axles in order to keep the center of gravity as low as possible The material used is steel tubing, aluminum and glass. It weighs 18 tons. The pusher-type four-bladed propeller is located at the extreme rear of the car and is driven by a 500 horse-power motor. It is maintaining a regular schedule of over 100 miles per hour and has, ever since it was built.

North German Lloyd

23 · S. S. BREMEN

DESIGNED BY DEUTSCHE SHIFF &
MASCHINENBAU A. G. WERK A. G. WESER 1928

[33]

It is the fastest car on rails that has ever been built, and it has lived up to its specifications. I don't predict that it will come into general use on American roads. It is an experimental project that worked out successfully and indicates a tendency in future railway design. The fact that it is streamlined, of light construction, with a low center of gravity, has more to do with its speed than its airplane motor propeller. It would be relatively simple to apply the same principle to an entire train as well as to one car.

We can foresee the time when motor boats will be approaching a speed of one hundred and fifty miles or more an hour. This is not at all improbable, though the goal will not be achieved soon. With the motor boat, unquestionably, will rest the record for speed on water. Neither the liner nor cruiser can be considered as its rival. Even if the difficulties in the way of forcing the giant liner up to a speed of one hundred miles per hour should prove physically possible of solution, the problem is nevertheless commercially insuperable. The fastest liners such as the Bremen and Europa have not yet exceeded the thirty-knot mark except for short distances, though warships have attained faster speeds.

As an example of organic design and its influence on the visual form let us consider the ship. From time immemorial up to the present moment the ship has always been one of the most fascinating of objects and to a great many people one of the most beautiful. It has probably aroused as much satisfaction as any work of man. This applies to nearly all types of ships. But in particular I am thinking of such famous styles as the clipper ship,[21] the four-masted schooner and the steam liner.[22] It would be easy to include such picturesque types as the sampan. The clipper ships were the liners of their day and the fastest commercial sailing ships ever built. The fastest crossing on record between America and Europe was twelve days and six hours.

What we've always liked about ships is that they have been first, last and always *ships*. The ship has had the same logical development at the hands of men of the sea as the airplane has had at the hands of men of the air. For years, when aboard ship, if you are observing, you have seen better modern architecture (in 1932 terms) than you have ashore.[24] But the ship has recently suffered a reactionary change that is disturbing. Commercial minds, reasoning that many people when traveling aboard ship like to forget they are at sea, have built all over the interior of the ship a lot of decorations in imitation of baronial halls and the like. They have endeavored to make ships into floating hotels. This is as illogical as painting stripes on a horse and calling it a zebra. The quality that has for generations stood out and made us love ships is the style and character that has been a natural development, without affectation. Now, shall we take this quality away from ships?

24 · S. S. CONTE BIANCAMANO   DESIGNED BY ANSOLDO SHIPBUILDING CO. 1924

Ewing Galloway

As an extreme illustration of the tendency just mentioned, I have in mind one of the largest liners, the Belgenland, which recently did over its decks to make them look like streets and alleys in a quaint little continental town!

The newer ships of the French and German lines are nearly as bad in a different way. They have merely used a different *mode* of interior decoration. Instead of being in the style of twenty years ago, they are in the so-called style of to-day, which is, in its general application, worse. A definite activity on the part of artists in all fields towards designing on the basis of functional requirements and the elimination of unessentials is the heart of the modern movement. For every artist in any field there are a hundred others who, not satisfied at being good craftsmen, make broader claims for themselves. These are the workers who depend on ornament to solve any problem. At the present moment Europe and America are deluged with this slang version of modern design. Actually it is the direct opposite of modern design. It has most of the faults of that great period of atrocities, the Victorian era, and in addition is vulgar and totally lacking in charm. Do not misunderstand my point. I am not urging that a modern liner be treated as one would a schooner; that portholes should replace windows, for instance. Nothing of the sort. A modern liner should be built along the most advanced lines. Twenty-five years ago portholes were the solution. To-day they are unnecessary. A whole deck may be glassed in as occasion demands. There is actually no difference between a porthole and a small window, except that a porthole is round and a window is

Maurice Goldberg

rectangular. What I do object to is the application of land-architecture instead of continuing the development of ship-architecture in its own organic terms.

Now let us consider some of the problems involved in correctly designing the steamship for the needs of to-day. By comparison with a 500-mile-an-hour airplane, the ocean liner is a slow-moving mode of transport. But speed is a *relative* thing. One cannot discuss the speed of a racehorse with that of a bullet. Nevertheless, the world still recognizes that Man o' War was undeniably fast!

The Bremen,[22] although she broke the speed record held by the Mauretania for some 15 years, exceeded the speed of the Mauretania by a very small margin. The Mauretania crossed

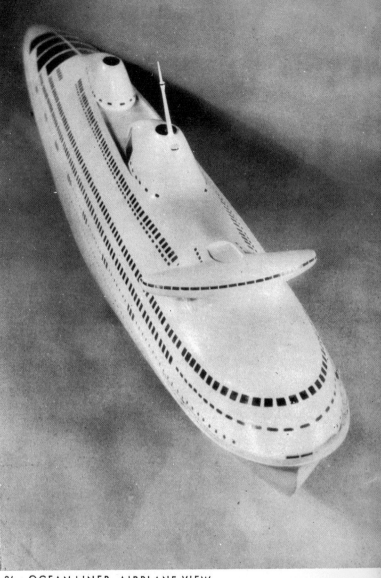

Maurice Goldberg

26 · OCEAN LINER: AIRPLANE VIEW
DESIGNED BY NORMAN BEL GEDDES 1932

from Ambrose to Plymouth, 3083 nautical miles in 4 days, 17 hours and 49 minutes, an average speed of 27.2 knots. The Bremen crossed from Ambrose to Cherbourg in 4 days, 14 hours, an average speed of 28.8 knots. Traveling a distance of 3175 nautical miles from Cherbourg Breakwater to Ambrose Lightship, the Europa beat the Bremen by only 9 minutes. The Europa is only 1.6 knots faster than the Mauretania. Thus, it is easily seen that in the Blue Ribbon speed contest on the Atlantic, small gains assume immense importance.

It is conceded that steamships will eventually make considerably better speed than now. But before they reach fifty knots, the practice now regarded more or less as axiomatic among marine engineers will have changed considerably. Some of the problems involved are obvious: a hull and a superstructure offering a minimum of resistance to water and air, and a greater ratio of motive power for each unit of weight. Every protruding form such as deck housings, ventilating funnels, stacks, lifeboats, no matter if as small as a cable, offers a wind-resisting surface and rear vacuum that in a form as large as a ship reaches an enormous total.[23]

Consistent with these principles, I have designed an ocean liner 1808 feet in length, with a molded depth of 120 feet, beam 110 feet, and approximately 70,000 tons displacement. Streamlined as to both hull and superstructure, it is designed for luxurious accommodations, economy of operation, and increased speed performance. It is a steamship that can be built and operated under existing conditions. Accommodations are provided for 2000 first-class passengers, and for a crew of 900 men. What I have sought for in this design has resulted in a radical departure from general practice.

The entire superstructure is streamlined.[25] Every air pocket of any kind whatsoever has been eliminated. All projections have either been eliminated or enclosed within the streamlined shell. The single protrusion is the navigator's bridge and this is cantilevered and similar in shape to a monoplane wing, consequently offering a minimum of resistance to the air. The smoke-

27 · OCEAN LINER: STERN DECKS CLOSED   DESIGNED BY NORMAN BEL GEDDES 1932

stacks are a radical departure in appearance. They are oval on the inside, but on the outside, due to streamlining, they dissolve into the mass form of the ship almost to the point of disappearing.[25] The streamlined foil of the forward stack contains a café, with dance floor, orchestra and bar. The streamlined foil of the rear stack is a hangar and machine shop for two trimotored seaplanes.

Lifeboats are within the skin of the ship instead of being hung on an exposed deck.[26] There are twenty-four of them, each accommodating one hundred and fifty persons. They are of the unsinkable type, completely enclosed, equipped with radio apparatus, and two weeks' concentrated rations. The boat deck is isolated from passenger use except in case of emergency.[39] Its central portion is the upper space of the public social rooms. When the lifeboats are to be used, a section of the side of the boat deck hinges out to a position level with the deck and so forms a gangway.[28] Two steel davits run out horizontally, carrying the lifeboat with them and lowering it to a position flush with the gangways. The gangways have railings on all sides with a gate in the center, so that passengers can not fall off in the excitement. Passengers walk from the deck, across the gangway and directly into the boat. The

28 · OCEAN LINER: STERN DECKS OPENED   DESIGNED BY NORMAN BEL GEDDES 1932

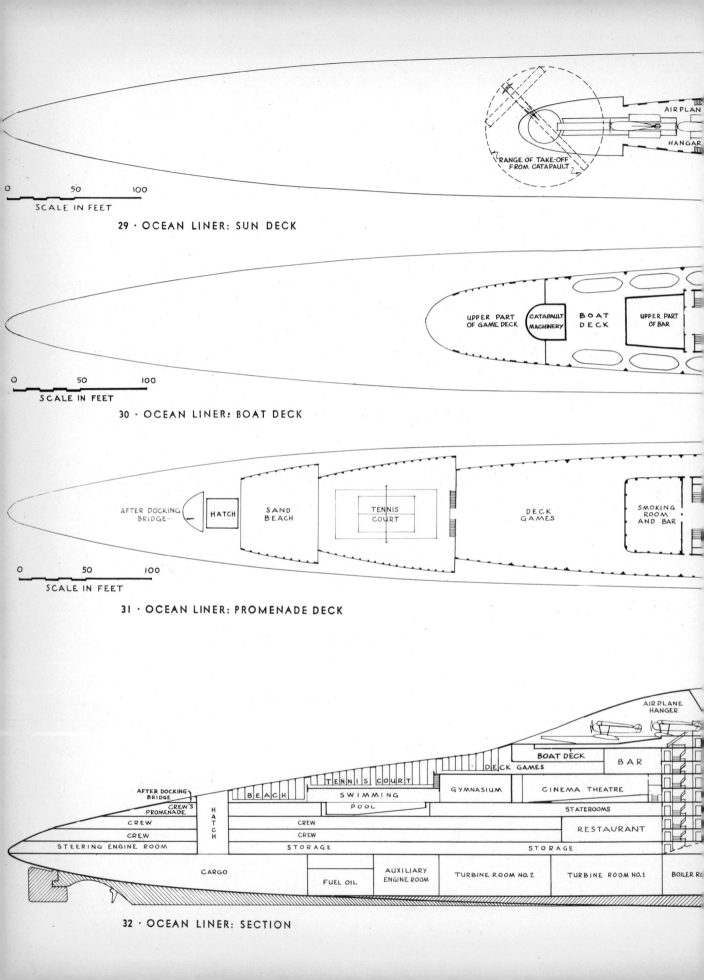

AIRPLANE

HANGAR

RANGE OF TAKE-OFF
FROM CATAPULT

0   50   100
SCALE IN FEET

29 · OCEAN LINER: SUN DECK

UPPER PART
OF GAME DECK | CATAPULT
MACHINERY | BOAT
DECK | UPPER PART
OF BAR

0   50   100
SCALE IN FEET

30 · OCEAN LINER: BOAT DECK

AFTER DOCKING
BRIDGE — | HATCH | SAND
BEACH | TENNIS
COURT | DECK
GAMES | SMOKING
ROOM
AND BAR

0   50   100
SCALE IN FEET

31 · OCEAN LINER: PROMENADE DECK

AIRPLANE
HANGER

BOAT DECK | BAR

DECK GAMES

AFTER DOCKING
BRIDGE
CREW'S
PROMENADE | BEACH | TENNIS COURT | GYMNASIUM | CINEMA THEATRE

SWIMMING
POOL | STATEROOMS

HATCH

CREW | CREW | RESTAURANT

CREW | CREW

STEERING ENGINE ROOM | STORAGE | STORAGE

CARGO | FUEL OIL | AUXILIARY
ENGINE ROOM | TURBINE ROOM NO. 2 | TURBINE ROOM NO. 1 | BOILER RO

32 · OCEAN LINER: SECTION

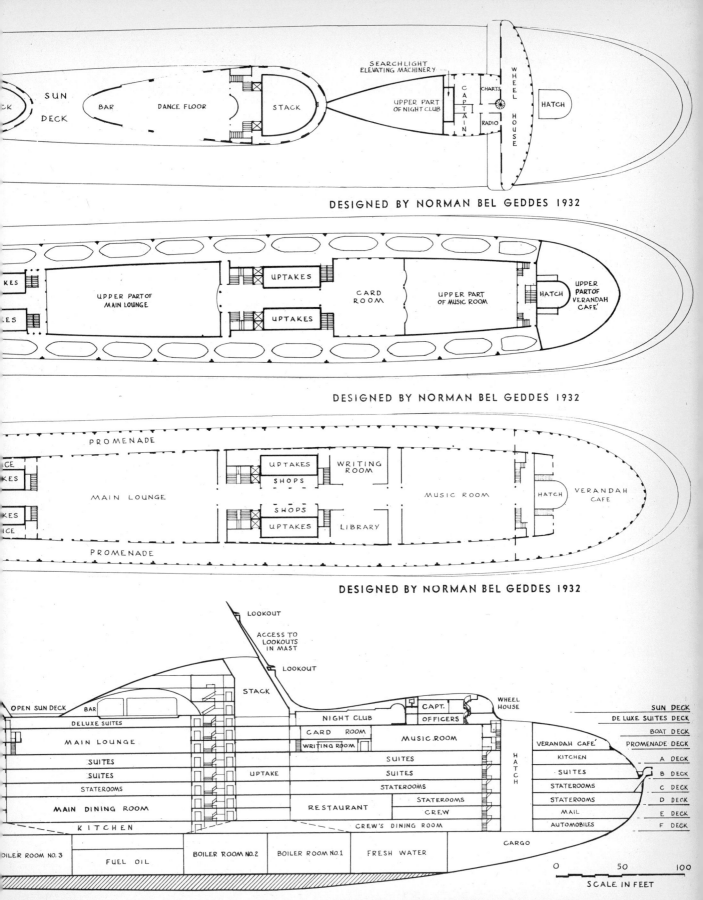

SUN DECK BAR DANCE FLOOR STACK

SEARCHLIGHT ELEVATING MACHINERY

UPPER PART OF NIGHT CLUB CAPTAIN CHARTS RADIO WHEEL HOUSE HATCH

DESIGNED BY NORMAN BEL GEDDES 1932

UPPER PART OF MAIN LOUNGE UPTAKES UPTAKES CARD ROOM UPPER PART OF MUSIC ROOM HATCH UPPER PART OF VERANDAH CAFE

DESIGNED BY NORMAN BEL GEDDES 1932

PROMENADE

MAIN LOUNGE UPTAKES SHOPS WRITING ROOM SHOPS UPTAKES LIBRARY MUSIC ROOM HATCH VERANDAH CAFE

PROMENADE

DESIGNED BY NORMAN BEL GEDDES 1932

LOOKOUT
ACCESS TO LOOKOUTS IN MAST
LOOKOUT
STACK
OPEN SUN DECK BAR
DELUXE SUITES
MAIN LOUNGE
SUITES
SUITES
STATEROOMS
MAIN DINING ROOM
KITCHEN
BOILER ROOM NO. 3 FUEL OIL BOILER ROOM NO. 2 BOILER ROOM NO. 1 FRESH WATER
NIGHT CLUB
CARD ROOM
WRITING ROOM
UPTAKE
RESTAURANT
CREW'S DINING ROOM
CAPT.
OFFICERS
MUSIC ROOM
SUITES
SUITES
STATEROOMS
STATEROOMS
CREW
WHEEL HOUSE
HATCH
CARGO
VERANDAH CAFE
KITCHEN
SUITES
STATEROOMS
STATEROOMS
MAIL
AUTOMOBILES

SUN DECK
DE LUXE SUITES DECK
BOAT DECK
PROMENADE DECK
A DECK
B DECK
C DECK
D DECK
E DECK
F DECK

0 50 100
SCALE IN FEET

DESIGNED BY NORMAN BEL GEDDES 1932

same switch on the bridge that rings the alarm gongs over the ship simultaneously opens all hatchways to the boat deck, opens up the side of this deck and automatically puts each boat into position for loading.

Naturally, there is a relationship between the exterior contour of the ship and its internal arrangement. The skin of the ship is so designed that in rough weather, when the going is difficult and it would ordinarily require considerably increased engine power to offset a sixty-mile-an-hour wind, the entire form, including all deck area, is enclosed in a streamline form.[27] At such times all air is mechanically conditioned. The movable elements of this outer skin are in the form of light alloy or glass panels that slide or roll up. Although on stormy days the ship is as enclosed as a submarine, on pleasant days she is more open than the present liner.[28] Among other open deck features she has an unobstructed play deck equal in area to four full-size tennis courts. The very large swimming pool, although under cover, is adjacent to the open air and a large sun-exposed sand beach.[32]

My aim has been to design a hull which offers least resistance to the water and a superstructure offering least resistance to the air. As regards the former, experiments have shown that the aim is accomplished by a hull design giving an even wave line and having the least wetted surface. In this connection, one of the latest developments is the Maier hull, which has consistently shown an increase of some ten to twelve per cent efficiency over the ordinary hull. Experiments with models and records of wind resistance of ships under actual operating conditions indicate that the speed of a ship like the Mauretania is reduced fifteen per cent in a sixty-mile gale. While the results of experiments in the streamlining of ship superstructures are very meager in quantity, data on other objects moving in air show that streamlining permits a reduction of air resistance of some eighty per cent.

Since a ship is essentially a slow-moving object, compared with an automobile, and since the resistance varies with the square of the speed, this figure of eighty per cent is high except on the basis of extraordinary head winds. Such winds create high seas which increase the wave resistance. Future experiments will doubtless show that this circumstance offsets much of the saving due to streamlining the superstructure. In my opinion, the possible saving due to this feature in the present design is about fourteen per cent over the normal superstructure.

According to calculations, this liner should not only be more economical to build and operate than the fastest liner now in service, but she should, in addition, cut transatlantic steamship time by about one day. With a twenty per cent increase in speed, which appears to be a thoroughly reasonable esti- mate, the saving in time between New York and Plymouth would be twenty- two hours, an average speed of five and three-quarter knots greater than that of the Europa. This comparison becomes the greater in bad weather, for this ship is primarily designed to offset high winds and seas.

CHAPTER 3

Motor Cars and Buses

DRIVING to-day's motor car is a peculiar experience for one who understands in the least degree the principles of aërodynamics; for he realizes that the mechanism under his control is so inadequately designed from this viewpoint that it would be more efficient if it were operated with the rear end to the front.[19B]

Put your hand out of the window of a car traveling at thirty miles an hour, and gauge the force of the wind resistance. Do the same at sixty miles an hour. Compare, for the sake of a rough guess, the area of your hand with the total area of the car opposed to the same pressure. In this, you have the basis for a rough calculation of the tremendous inefficiency, in one respect, of to-day's motor car. Only realize, in addition, that the partial vacuum caused by projections such as lamps and fenders, abrupt steps or changes in contour such as the windshield, and the vacuum at the rear of the body itself more than doubles the resistance caused by the wind pressure at the front.

The subject of aërodynamics is anything but simple. Some applications of its principles, however, are not difficult to define. An object is *airfoiled* when its exterior surface is so designed that upon being projected through air, a useful dynamic reaction is imparted to the object by the action of the air. The lift of an airplane wing is an excellent example of a useful dynamic reaction. An object is *streamlined* when its exterior surface is so designed that upon passing through a fluid such as water or air the object creates the least disturbance in the fluid in the form of eddies or partial vacua tending to produce resistance. In other words, an object is airfoiled in order to *create* a

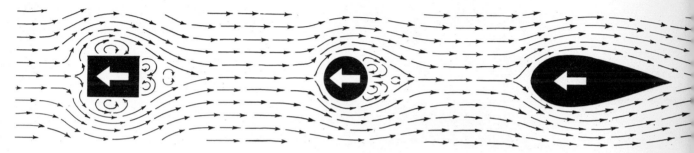

33 · DIAGRAM ILLUSTRATING THE PRINCIPLE OF STREAMLINING

disturbance and an object is streamlined in order to *eliminate* disturbances in the media through which they pass.

It is well known that a drop of water falling in still air assumes an almost perfect streamline form. This form is approximately that of an egg, though the small end of the drop tapers more sharply to a conical point. In falling, the larger and blunt end of the drop is foremost. This is the shape that creates the least turbulence in the form of eddies and partial vacua which increase wind resistance.[33] A stationary sand bar or sheet of ice in a fast-moving stream takes on a streamline form due to the water's action in passing.[34] A strut or wire, as on an airplane, has twenty times the resistance of a streamlined form having the same thickness as the diameter of

34 · SHEET OF ICE IN FLOWING STREAM DEMONSTRATING NATURE'S STREAMLINING

Manfred Curry

[45]

the wire but tapered out to a length of about three diameters, merely because it eliminates the rear vacuum."

Theoretically, then, streamlining requires that the broadest part of the motor car be at the front and that all surfaces and projections which create eddies or cause retarding suction should be eliminated. Various experiments have proved the validity of this theory. It is an established fact that the motor car of to-day going at forty miles per hour uses sixty per cent of the engine's power in overcoming wind resistance.

Automotive engineers understand the fundamentals necessary for solving the problem of wind resistance. But motor-car manufacturers have never encouraged their engineers to

35 · AMPHIBIAN PLANE   DESIGNED BY SIKORSKY

tackle the problem, not at least in the thorough-going manner that airplane manufacturers have been forced to. The hesitancy of the motor-car manufacturer is based upon the theory that the public likes the appearance of present-day cars and would not like one completely streamlined. They are willing to make the necessary change after some one else has taken the lead. In the automobile industry the situation with regard to streamlining is similar to that which formerly existed with regard to lowering the center of gravity. For years there was talk about the necessity of lowering the motor car's center of gravity, but manufacturers waited for the other fellow to do it first. Mr. Cord did it. Immediately, the others followed.

When automobile manufacturers first found themselves in need of bodies for chassis, they naturally appealed to the designers of horse-drawn carriages.[36] What the carriage designers offered had most of the main characteristics of the vehicle on which they had previously concentrated their attention. Gradually new features such as the windshield were added, and the whole structure became heavier.[37] When the public showed a preference for the closed car, the design of motor-car bodies greatly improved. But it was not until after the War that designers and manufacturers made a determined effort to abandon carriage ideas.

The narrow point of view that some of the various companies take is the influential factor in the design of to-day's motor car. Basic changes are expensive and to justify themselves must be unusually successful. Possibly executives find it difficult to maintain a perspective, owing to the fact that they are surrounded by subordinates who reflect rather than stimulate the executive's viewpoint. The executive may think that by minor changes here and there, after the manner of fashion designers with women's clothes, by changing the shape of moldings or of hardware, and by adding new gadgets, he is improving the design of the car. When visual design gives major emphasis to details, the result can only be mediocre.

Having successfully overcome the enormous difficulties involved in making the motor car work, the industry is now endeavoring to make it beautiful. This beauty is of a questionable sort. Stylistic in trend, it attacks the problem superficially, modishly. Between most of these stylistic alterations and their utility there is no direct relation.

A tendency towards simplification has been the dominant factor in the improved appearance of motor-car bodies in the past few years. A few motor cars on the market, although they do not represent my own beliefs, are nevertheless good-looking according to their own standards, and they are well designed up to that point. They are cars that do not make the seasonal changes which makers of cheap popular cars believe necessary.[38] A few makers of high-grade motor cars have over a period of years built a reputation by emphasizing two ideas — that their cars would be a long time in wearing out, and that they would not soon look out of date. If, in part, they have ceased to carry conviction, it is primarily because the design of the body is not sufficiently organic. Their *style* is applied — too much on the surface, too much a continuation of precedent, not sufficiently and inherently directed toward that of the ultimate motor car.[38]

For years I have observed trends in design at the National Automobile Show. One notices slight improvements, such as the slanting windshield and the radiator with rounded front. By a process of timid nibbling, manufacturers are slowly approaching the application of aërodynamic principles. Meanwhile, each succeeding show offers evidence, in the multiplication of gadgets and so-called selling points, that the end of an era has arrived. Scores of thousands of the interested public throng the show to greet the new. What they behold is something quite the opposite. For, the National Automobile Show, instead of offering truly progressive design, presents to the public the opportunity to inspect an assemblage of variants of a single type that is already obsolescent.

36 · MOTOR CAR   DESIGNED BY DR. DITTLINGER 1898

Automotive Industries

[48]

It is a surprising fact that the average automobile manufacturer believes that the general public not only enjoys but approves the show. If the manufacturer would listen to disinterested remarks, if he would detach himself from the influence of approving employees, he would discover that each year the public is hopeful but disappointed because, having read announcements of innovations and improvements, they do not find them except in minor instances. To-day's most advanced type of motor cars, with the exception of a few specially built racing models, are at least ten years behind the actual knowledge of the industry. On numerous occasions, I have discussed this topic with leading manufacturers and engineers in the industry; and I find that, when they divorce themselves sufficiently from current sales problems and speak frankly, they concur in at least a broad sense with what I am saying here.

One of the chief factors restraining the manufacturer from making more fundamental annual changes in his cars is the cost of tooling up and the cost of dies. To make a complete set of dies for a motor car requires a considerable expenditure of money. The present method is to alter annually as few dies as possible, sufficient however to make changes which will be noticed by the public, and which may be advertised as the new model. I do not imply that in the motor car of to-day, badly designed as it is from the viewpoint of function, there is not a certain stirring kind of appeal. In so far as it exists, it is the result of an attempt to make the motor car look its part.

37 · MOTOR CAR

DESIGNED BY VELIE 1908

Automotive Industries

But it can never exert the same force of appeal that the projectile-like racing car does until it is designed in accord with the same functional principles.

We admire the swordfish, seagull, greyhound, Arab stallion and Durham bull because they seem made to do their particular work. When the motor car, bus, truck and tractor have evolved into the essential forms determined by what these machines have to do, they will not need surface ornamentation to make them beautiful. Their beauty will be inherent and that will be all the beauty that they need. This is not meant to indicate that if the engineer

38 · MOTOR CAR

DESIGNED BY PACKARD 1932

Packard Motor Car Company

does his job well the result will be beautiful. Here is where the artist is essential, for he knows how to make a thing of beauty with the minimum of means. From this point on, he should be left alone. Prior to this point the two should work in close collaboration with each other. The artist should have complete freedom, assuming of course that he violates no engineering requirement. The final result must have the sincere approval of both — or something is wrong with it.

For the constantly recurrent offerings of ornate vehicles with minor improvements instead of motor cars expressive of their function, the public is held responsible on the ground that the public is slow to adjust itself to new impressions. I am convinced that the public is ahead of the manufacturer and eagerly awaiting that car which will look its part.

As one reason for this conviction, I cite the experience of a certain courageous manufacturer who not long since came out with his solution to the problem, a car with a front-wheel drive. The interest on the part of the public was unprecedented and this despite the car being in an expensive price class. Sales have not lived up to expectations, but this is due to other problems than the principle involved, or the response of the public. As is well known, one of the great advantages in owning a Ford is that you can find a Ford service station almost anywhere. The same condition exists to a certain extent with many other cars. But when the front-wheel-drive car came, with its radical departure from precedent, the public feared that in case of engine or other trouble they would have less chance of getting repairs made easily. Nevertheless, in spirit, the motoring public applauded Mr. Cord, and if his principle proves to be right the public will continue with him.

In conversation with automotive engineers and in the technical journals where they discuss shop, I frequently discover convincing evidence that they are restless over the present reactionary trend of motor-car design. I venture to say that among my criticisms there is not one that has not repeatedly been voiced by automotive designers who, by circumstances beyond their control, are compelled to continue producing designs that are far inferior to what they could accomplish if circumstances permitted the application of existing knowledge.

In the critical engineer's indictment of the present-day car, hardly any aspect escapes attention. The ratio of empty weight to useful load is extravagantly high. The power plant occupies the forward part of the chassis, the very position that should afford clear vision to the driver and the best sight-seeing advantages. By this position of the motor, the small car is deprived of roomy comfort. Furthermore, this position of the motor contributes directly to discomfort through vibration, odor, and excess heat in summer. Without success, I have tried to find one good reason why the power plant should monopolize space at the front. I am convinced that it is entirely the result of the horse-drawn vehicle precedent.

Distributed throughout the present-day car, as though by chance, are the most vital parts of the mechanism — engine, clutch, transmission, and differential. Presently it will be the obligation of designers to collect this miscellany and to arrange it organically into one unit. Possibly, even the rear wheels will be included in this unit.

We may anticipate a further great improvement — that the properly organized power unit will eventually be detachable without great difficulty. It will then be possible to leave your motor for repairs or overhauling, insert another unit, and have the use of your own car while the repair work is being done. In to-day's car there are too many points requiring attention and they are too widely separated. To illustrate: though most manufacturers recommend that the battery should be tested at least once a week, the battery is placed somewhere about the car in a position so difficult of access that one might infer the manufacturer's intention is to hide it. With the exception, possibly, of the engine, nearly all parts lack accessibility. Wheel suspension can justly be

39 · MOTOR CAR NUMBER I   DESIGNED BY NORMAN BEL GEDDES 1928

Maurice Goldberg

criticised. There is an excess of unsprung weight. Throughout the car as a whole, the distribution of weight is poor.

A wasteful characteristic of to-day's motor car is the space allowed for the overhang of mud guards. The width of to-morrow's car will undoubtedly be that of present-day mud guards with wheels inset in the body. Mud guards are destined to disappear entirely. Springs of an entirely new design are necessary. When these are developed, each wheel will be independently swung. New type springs and power plants will make possible the use of a lighter frame, which will be incorporated into the body structure. Most cars are now so low, as regards head room, that getting in and out is a matter of difficulty. A needed improvement is a type of forced draft ventilation, obviating the necessity of opening windows for air, to the extreme discomfort of the passenger. At a stroke, the designer can eliminate all moldings and reduce the number and cost of dies used in the making of the body parts.

A few years ago Glenn Curtiss, one of our foremost aviation designers, carried on a series of experiments with motor cars to ascertain the extent to which streamlining alone would increase their speed. He took a stock coupe, which as delivered from the factory ran at a maximum speed of seventy-four miles per hour,[39A] and removed the body superstructure. He replaced it on the chassis backwards and driving it with the same motor, he was able to increase the speed of the car to over eighty-seven miles an hour.[39B] He then built a trailer which weighed fifteen hundred pounds and fastened it to the rear of the car. The trailer was built in a streamline form to eliminate the vacuum at the rear of the coupe. Despite doubling the weight that the engine had to pull, the streamlining increased the speed of the car eleven per cent.[39C] Further tests by Curtiss proved that the speed of the average automobile could be increased twenty per cent when going only twenty-five miles an hour merely by streamlining. This ratio increases considerably as the speed increases.

Employing the principles of aërodynamics, I designed a motor car four years ago, and called it Car Number 5, meaning a car of five years from then. Working backward in four stages, we succeeded, by the time we came to Car Number 1, in designing an automobile which, except for its extreme simplicity, would resemble present-day cars.[40] It could be driven on the streets now without attracting attention other than casual admiration. Each of the five models represent a twenty per cent change over the previous one as each is advanced by degrees toward a definite ideal standard — not in

41 · MOTOR CAR NUMBER 8   DESIGNED BY NORMAN BEL GEDDES 1931

terms of transient modes. As the only ideas contained in these five models that have so far appeared (to my knowledge) in other cars, are in this Number 1 model, I am not illustrating the other four here.

That series of designs was developed for an average-priced car on an average wheel base. Automotive engineers have estimated that Car Number 1, as a result of the streamlining of the body, would make a speed of fifty-eight miles an hour with the same power as would be necessary to drive the existing rectangular car forty-five miles an hour. Other features of this car which up to that time were innovations are: the round front radiator, the top folding down into the body; the windshield sliding vertically into body, driving lights turning with front wheels, the fuel tank and trunk compartment built into the body; the license plate built into the basic design, and the elimination of all moldings.[40]

42 · MOTOR CAR NUMBER 8
DESIGNED BY NORMAN BEL GEDDES 1931

This car was designed for the then Graham-Paige Company (now the Graham Motor Car Company). Mr. Ray Graham was more instrumental than any other one person in encouraging me to enter the industrial field. The car was never built, owing to psychological factors in the human make-up that have to do with timidity. The design impressed his various department heads as a little extreme. Nevertheless, had the stock market crashed a week later in the fall of 1929 a first test body of Car Number 1 would have been built at a maximum cost of eight thousand dollars and tried out on the roads. For that expenditure there might have been on the market two years ago the first step towards a new idea in automotive design. With the crash, the pioneering spirit which prompted this particular undertaking departed.

I have since designed another series of cars, incorporating ideas other than streamlining and which has resulted in a radical departure from our present conception of a motor car.[41] The exterior shell of this series of cars is streamlined, other than on the ground side, to as near the drop form as is practicable. It is not designed for higher speed but for present-day speed with less power. Campbell's Bluebird was designed for the highest possible speed. The major problem in designing that car was to keep it from rising off the ground.

In the case of the present car, one of the main problems has been to reduce the power. Hence, the difference in design.

My design seeks to eliminate all projections as well as flat surfaces normal to the wind which tend to create resistance. In addition, increased convenience and seating capacity have been provided.

One of these motor cars is designed on a 116-inch wheel base which places it in the middle group as to size and price, comparable to the Oldsmobile,

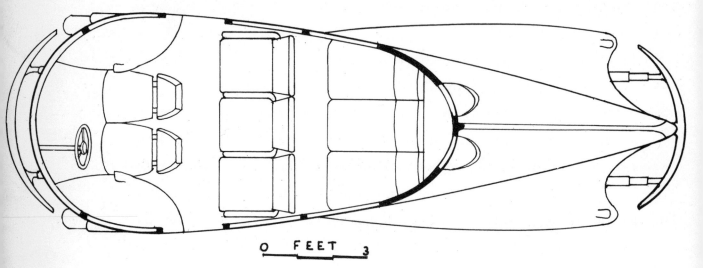

O FEET 3

43 · MOTOR CAR NUMBER 8: SECTION   DESIGNED BY NORMAN BEL GEDDES 1931

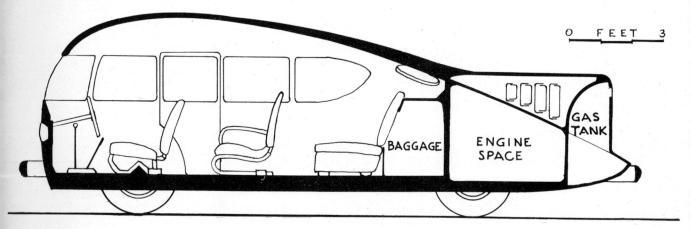

O FEET 3

BAGGAGE   ENGINE SPACE   GAS TANK

44 · MOTOR CAR NUMBER 8: PLAN   DESIGNED BY NORMAN BEL GEDDES 1931

De Soto, and the medium-size Buicks and Chryslers. However, instead of five, it carries eight passengers very comfortably.

Although the car is completely streamlined, and to a much further extent than any other non-racing motor car to date, certain modifications have been made in the drop-form theory. In general, this car represents a simplification of most of the experiments in the past and more nearly approaches a perfect streamline form, although ultimate efficiency in this respect is impossible. The body tapers off at the rear, allowing the air to slip past with the least disturbance. This one feature in contrast to the present-day conventional form eliminates the enormous air pocket which is created at the rear of to-day's enclosed car.[38] In the sedan of ordinary design, the air is actually eddying and whirling and holding back the progress of the car in varying amounts up to sixty per cent.

At first sight, you may not think this design looks pleasing or much like a motor car. You may think it odd. This results from the extent to which it is streamlined and to your being accustomed to the present type of motor car. Your grandparents would have felt the same way about the car you are driving. To myself and my staff the novelty of this Car Number 8 has worn off, and it appears more logical and attractive than present-day designs.

Numerous changes, some of them in the nature of innovations, have been made in keeping with the main objects of the design.[43] The bulk of the car is forward. Headlights are inset in the front and shine through a glass that is flush with the surface. The two lamps are operated as a single unit. They are connected with the steering gear and turn as the car turns, so that in rounding a curve or corner at night the light is not off to one side. There are two small lights at each extreme side that

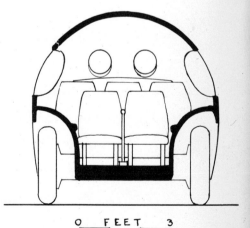

O   FEET   3

45 · MOTOR CAR NUMBER 8: SECTION
DESIGNED BY NORMAN BEL GEDDES 1931

mark the dimensions of the car and serve as parking lights. Mud guards have been eliminated. Wheels are enclosed in the body. Otherwise, in connection with the wheels, there are no innovations. The car is controlled from the extreme front. The steering wheel is located directly over the forward axle. The steering mechanism is greatly simplified and more easily serviced and repaired.

The engine is at the extreme rear and acts directly on the rear axle. This position makes it possible to centralize the power plant. With the elimination of the long transmission shaft, which is necessary when the engine is at the front, it becomes possible to lower the center of gravity, decreasing the danger of overturn when making curves at high speed. Placing the engine at the rear permits of better insulation against heat, noise

Bus Transportation

46 · EDWARDS MOTOR TRANSIT BUS   DESIGNED BY WHITE 1918

and fumes, and simplifies repairing and service operations. A water-cooled motor is specified. Air for radiator cooling is provided for by louvers which force the air where desired. They are at the sides over the wheels and at the rear in the stabilizing fin.

The interior design is purely functional. Increased seating space is the primary advantage.[44] Eight passengers may be seated as follows: Two in individual front seats (driver and passenger); three in center chairs; three in the rear lounge. Complete visibility is provided for the driver and all passengers.[45] Neither engine hood, fenders or head lamps can obstruct it. The windows extend without interruption entirely around the car. The window area is at least twenty per cent greater than that of conventional cars in the same class. Ventilation without draft is provided through louvers at the front. Air, coming through these louvers is conveyed between the outer shell and the insulation which forms the interior finish of the car. The air is distributed through grills.

The idea of bus transportation was introduced in 1905. The buses were merely elongated touring cars.[46] Although the buses of to-day look big, roomy and comfortable, all that I have ridden in are distinctly uncomfortable. The Pickwick Duplex Coach is said to represent the most advanced bus design at the present time.[47] It does not permit a passenger to relax any more than to-day's airplane cabin does. Instead, you are continually bracing yourself against road shocks and jolts. These are among the disadvantages that I have endeavored to eliminate in my designs for buses.

The same reasons for streamlining apply to the bus as to the motor car.[48] It will result in greater speed at less engine power and in smoother riding qualities. The stabilizing fin, which is essential to prevent the rear from swinging when going at high rates of speed, contains the gasoline tank.[49] Its gasoline capacity is sufficient to enable the bus to go from New York to Detroit (at four miles per gallon) without refueling. The weight of the fuel, even though it is variable, is, along with the weight of the engine, an important traction and stabilizing factor. The engine is over the rear axle, and at one side to facilitate servicing and to give passengers ready access to the observation lounge.[51]

47 · PICKWICK DUPLEX COACH   DESIGNED BY DWIGHT E. AUSTIN 1931

Bus Transportation

Instead of the customary two wheels for steering in front there are four.[48] This decreases the load per tire and increases the safety factor. If one of the forward tires blows out, the car, instead of swerving suddenly, continues to ride on three forward wheels, until it is convenient to replace the damaged wheel. Two spare wheels are carried in a compartment on the ceiling of the lower deck over the engine. The body design eliminates the necessity for a chassis.

The large baggage compartment on the rear upper deck is reached by ladders and may be opened from either side of the bus. It contains sufficient space to store baggage systematically.[52] There are two doors on the right side, one forward by the driver and another in the center.[48] The driver can open or close both doors automatically without leaving his seat. I believe this is the only double-deck bus for interstate travel in which the space directly under the upper deck is utilized for seating passengers. The deck arrangement is similar to that of the heavy transit buses used only in urban transportation, such as the Fifth Avenue buses in New York. But buses of the type used on Fifth Avenue are too high, top-heavy, and unstable for high-speed transit.

Although the seating arrangement of the two decks is, in many ways, similar to the typical city bus, the over-all height has been lowered two feet.[52] As the center of gravity is lower, it is not top-heavy. The form has a great deal to do with permitting this improvement. The reduced floor level of the lower deck, made possible to a great extent by the elimination of the drive shaft

DESIGNED BY NORMAN BEL GEDDES 1932

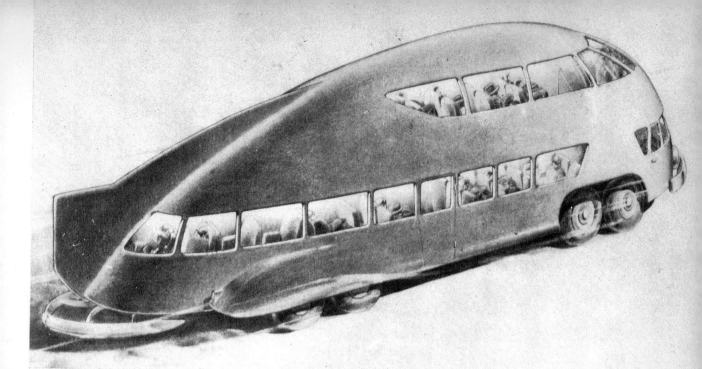

and other mechanisms under the floor (since the engine is located over the rear axle), lowers the center of gravity. A comfort advantage resulting from this lower center of gravity, is greater road stability. The wheel base of the bus is two hundred and fifty inches. It accommodates fifty-three persons, including driver and steward. The lower deck seats thirty-three persons;[1] the upper deck twenty.[50] This seating capacity exceeds by twenty the average seating capacity of conventional buses with the same wheel base and is greater than that in any bus of equal cubic content yet designed. Twenty per cent more space is allowed per passenger than in any bus to-day. This increase in capacity has been obtained by an increase in width and body length. Even with these increases the bus still conforms to the present road statutes.[3] With only two exceptions, there are no seats directly over the wheels.

The stairway to the second deck is over the right front wheels. Under these stairs is an especially designed lavatory and toilet.[51] Opposite this stairway is a buffet equipped with generous refrigerator, electric range and other facilities for serving light hot or cold meals, drinks and ice-cream soda. A table can be installed in front of any chair as in a present-day Pullman car. A news-stand display is provided for on top of the engine compartment.[51] In the rear is an observation lounge, with seats facing the rear. No seat on either deck has any obstruction to prevent the passenger from looking out in all directions. Window mullions are so spaced that all of them come between seats rather than in the line of vision. The interior decorations are quiet and restful. All lighting is indirect. A radio is included. Air-conditioning equipment is specified which would eliminate tobacco smoke immediately.

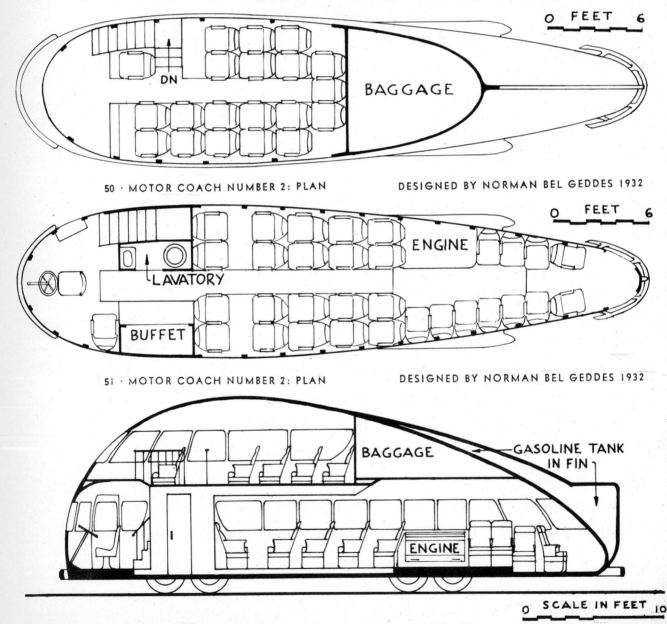

O FEET 6

BAGGAGE

DN

50 · MOTOR COACH NUMBER 2: PLAN   DESIGNED BY NORMAN BEL GEDDES 1932

O FEET 6

ENGINE

LAVATORY

BUFFET

51 · MOTOR COACH NUMBER 2: PLAN   DESIGNED BY NORMAN BEL GEDDES 1932

BAGGAGE

GASOLINE TANK IN FIN

ENGINE

O SCALE IN FEET 10

52 · MOTOR COACH NUMBER 2: SECTION   DESIGNED BY NORMAN BEL GEDDES 1932

In manufacture, on a mass production basis, the designs for these motor cars and buses offer considerable opportunities for economies owing to simplified fabrication, less exterior surface and centralized mechanical design.

In the early days of the automobile, manufacturers concerned themselves only with making the machine go. Of late years, having succeeded with the first objective, the manufacturer has given his attention to such matters as comfort and appearance. It is my prediction that within the next two or three years some farseeing manufacturer will again turn his attention to making his machine go, that this time his design will be the result of what has been learned in this motorized-buggy era. This means that he will start afresh and that his objective will be the ultimate form of the future motor car. This car will look very different from those you see on the road to-day but not very different from Car Number 8 as illustrated here. It will take the public about two years to accept the idea but they will do it for the simple reason that the basis for it is right. Then all the other manufacturers will follow this pioneer, but they will never reap the reward he will. It is the names of Columbus, Boone, Hamilton, Wright, Wanamaker, Ford, Lindbergh that mean something to us — not those of their trailers. It is the same with merchandising. The consuming mass has imagination and admiration. They like the new idea that is better than the old one and they idolize the fellow who blazed the way for it.

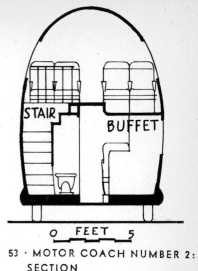

53 · MOTOR COACH NUMBER 2: SECTION
NORMAN BEL GEDDES 1932

CHAPTER 4

Railways

Though the future of the railroads is under debate, they still are and for a long time will be the backbone of American industrial life. The railroads represent one quarter of the total wealth of the country. They are not going out of business. The present emergency will pass. Rail mergers may be expected to solve many difficulties. Coming developments and innumerable improvements now on the way will solve others. Presently, prospects for the railroads will brighten.

In the past ten years the railroads have cut their costs. They are now becoming active in control and operation of competitive forms of transportation. Meanwhile, their freight business has remained stationary. Mileage has not increased. Loss in passenger revenues amounts to one third. A considerable proportion of the losses may be attributed to inroads of commercial motor transportation.

In our transportation system there is a definite place for the motor truck. A new public servant, it happens at the moment to exist and profit at the expense of taxpayers, and is permitted to operate under conditions that are not permitted the less favored railroads. The Class I railroads of the country, during 1930, spent thirteen and a half per cent. of their gross revenues in maintaining their right of way in good condition. This right of way represents billions of invested capital on which a fair return should be earned. Under existing conditions, for a competitive form of transportation, motor trucks and motor coaches, a right of way is provided out of public funds. Commercial motor transportation is presumably undertaxed at the moment, and this is one of the reasons for its rapid growth at the expense of the older systems. Eventually, when a more equitable adjustment exists, it will tend to restore the railroads to their proper place in the transportation scheme.

The railroads have been accused of lack of foresight. There are, of course, two sides to this. Innovations in railroading have been continuous. Some of the most important, up to 1900, were the heavy rail, the electric-block system, the so-called palace car, the steel car, and the compressed-air brake. Though it was then predicted that rail transport had reached its peak, railroad travel increased steadily. Improvements were likewise steady.

At one time, the rail weighing 90 pounds to the yard was considered adequate for main line tracks. To-day, the leading roads use a 130-pound rail, while the Pennsylvania recently announced the adoption of a 142-pound rail. With improved plates, these heavy rails have enormous strength and resistance to bending. They make for easier riding and are likewise a great factor for safety.

Highly important are improvements that have gone into the remaking of the road bed. Grade crossings and curves in untold numbers have been eliminated, grades have been reduced, the radii of curves that could not be eliminated have been substantially enlarged. The banking of the tracks on curves has been made a matter of accuracy. Ballasting is cleaner and more perfect. To-day, every standard road has a track-indicator car equipped with instruments which record the exact location of uneven points in the track. Block-signal and switching systems have been improved. By means of an electric contactor system, the engine is automatically stopped if it runs past a stop signal. Another electric device, valuable as an aid in helping trains keep on time in winter, is a heating coil that can be laid around the moving parts of a switch to eliminate snow and ice. To some extent noise and vibration have

Baltimore & Ohio R. R.

54 · BALTIMORE & OHIO LOCOMOTIVE   DESIGNED BY WILLIAM MASON 1856

been reduced by inserting rubber heels at all points where the frame rests. At the ends of the springs there are thick rubber pads — fifty-one of them in a six-wheel truck.

Some roads, including the New York Central and the Canadian National, have made extensive experiments with gasoline or oil-burning types of loco-motives. In locomotives of this design the engine does not directly communi-cate power to the movement of the unit, but operates a dynamo. The current is applied to turn the wheels upon the rails. This design, when perfected, will have a good deal to recommend it. Each locomotive will be a self-contained power unit, having its own generating station, thus eliminating the neces-sity for expensive power houses and transmission lines. Electric installation can then be extended to lines on which traffic is light as well as to heavily congested lines. Such locomotives will have greatly increased facility for quick and easy movement.

As yet, locomotives of this type are nowhere near perfection and are too expensive to operate. For the time being, at least, the railroads must rely upon the steam locomotive. For more than a hundred years, this mechanism has

55 · BALTIMORE & OHIO LOCOMOTIVE   DESIGNED BY BALDWIN LOCOMOTIVE WORKS 1923

been remarkably developed and perfected. In 1856 William Mason designed " the most beautiful as well as the most efficient locomotive."[4]

The modern steam locomotive in passenger service weighs three times as much as the locomotive of twenty years ago, and has three times the tractive effort. In length, it appears to have reached the maximum at an even hundred feet.[5] With its tender, it weighs more than eight hundred and fifty tons. Superheated steam is used at high boiler pressure — two hundred and fifty pounds. Firing is automatic. The London and North Eastern recently placed in passenger service a 4-6-4 type locomotive of semi-streamline design.[6] The exterior design is the result of experiments with a wooden model in a wind tunnel which were conducted with wind velocities equivalent to a locomotive speed of fifty miles per hour.

Prophets of disaster for the railroads declare that if they show the same lack of foresight in the future that they have in the past, they will presently become as obsolete as canals. This is a graphic way of putting a half-truth. I have taken considerable space to depict the advances made in railroading on the technical or engineering side as this concerns operation. As already noted, steady improvements in American railroads have been mainly for efficiency and safety, rather than for the comfort and convenience of passengers. In the latter respect there has been a lamentable lack of foresight. Changes in design intended to make good this deficiency have not been sufficiently radical. The

56 : LONDON & NORTH EASTERN LOCOMOTIVE   DESIGNED BY H. N. GRISLEY 1929

International News Photos

bedroom sleeper that the railroads recently put in service is, for instance, better than some previous arrangements, but it is far from meeting the standards of comfort and convenience required by to-day's traveling public. This sleeper has a drop-leaf table, lavatory, thermos bottle and shoe locker, which opens into the corridor. But it still retains its upper berth and is cramped.

The new type of seat of the day coaches would seem to represent an idea of improvement with the emphasis upon economy. Actually, it is a pair of seats, somewhat narrow and not particularly comfortable. It appears to be a survival of the idea that day coaches should be built as cheaply as possible, and

57 · LOCOMOTIVE NUMBER 1   DESIGNED BY NORMAN BEL GEDDES 1931

aim at maximum capacity rather than comfort. Eventually, to offset the competition of the bus, the railroads must offer a type of service which the bus cannot equal. Their greatest opportunity is in offering space and comfort.

Speed will increase as weight and wind resistance are reduced. Both factors are being experimented with at the present moment. In designing a train, I have utilized aluminum for the body of the cars, have lowered the height of the cars a foot and a half. This combination lowers the center of gravity, which lessens the possibility of tipping at high speeds. Streamlining, applied

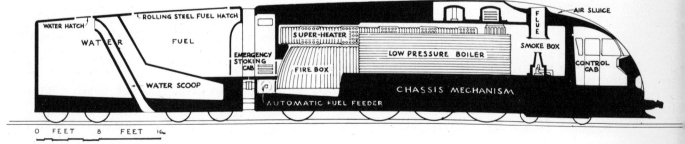

58 : LOCOMOTIVE NUMBER 1: SECTION   DESIGNED BY NORMAN BEL GEDDES 1931

Maurice Goldberg

59 · LOCOMOTIVE NUMBER 1
DESIGNED BY
NORMAN BEL GEDDES 1931

to the maximum throughout the train, eliminates air resistance and suctions. However, due to the extreme length of a train of ten passenger cars, in comparison with the possible maximum width and maximum height, a train does not offer the most efficient mass for streamlining.

Applying streamline principles to the locomotive produces a sound form which, if it strikes you as unusual, is brought about by the absence of the exposed stack, pipes, headlights, steam drum, cylinders, and projecting rear open cab. All these, in this design, are enclosed in a smooth steel and glass shell.[57] All points requiring frequent oiling or other attention are accessible by means of rolling metal shutters, which, when closed, conform to the streamlined contour of the shell.[57] The driving cab of the locomotive is located at the front instead of the rear.[57] This has been done to give the engineer maximum vision and to eliminate the risk of temporary interference with his vision by smoke and steam. His instrument board with its various controls is before him. The engine is provided with a full automatic stoking mechanism. There is a small cab at the rear of the locomotive, for use by the fireman only if the automatic stoker gets out of order.[58]

At the other end of the train, the rear car has been tapered off to allow the air to pass without forming an eddy.[61] All cars of the train have been designed to give the least resistance by the elimination of surfaces which tend to produce even small vacua. Such elements as exterior window sills, moldings, pipes, and vents, have been eliminated.[66] The tender and cars have a smooth, rounded contour. The telescoping bellows connection between

[70]

60 · REAR (OBSERVATION) CAR   DESIGNED BY PULLMAN COMPANY 1924

the cars is brought out much nearer the outside shell of the cars and is covered
with a smooth, elastic covering.[61] All glass is shatter proof and all windows
hermetically sealed.

Since the summer of 1931, on trains between New York and Washington,
the Baltimore and Ohio has tested the practicability of air conditioning. Previously, because of inconvenient terminal facilities in New York, this road
had not figured prominently in the New York-Washington passenger business. Owing to air cooling, its share in this business immediately increased to
a degree that has attracted the attention of all alert railroad executives. The
success of the venture definitely indicates widespread if not universal use of
not only air-conditioning equipment, but the public's reaction to more comfortable traveling conditions — even in the worst economic period in history,
when most executives believe no new expenditure is justifiable.

The cost of air conditioning on the Baltimore and Ohio trains is approxi-

[71]

mately twenty cents per day per passenger. Owing to the fact that air cooling is incorporated at the start in my design, the cost of maintaining this feature would be somewhat lessened. The present design calls for the steam-vacuum cooling method of the Carrier Engineering Company. This system requires less steam for cooling the car in summer than for heating the car in winter. Thus, the locomotive steam load is not increased. The fact that it is now feasible to supply railway cars with conditioned air is sufficiently remarkable,

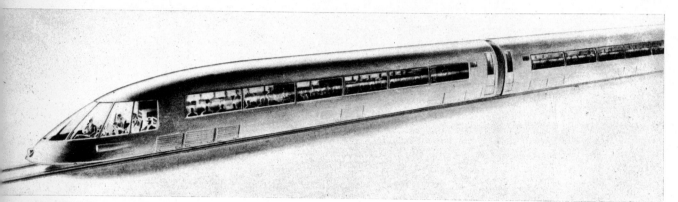

61 · REAR (LOUNGE) CAR NUMBER 4   DESIGNED BY NORMAN BEL GEDDES 1931

particularly when we recall that air-conditioning systems for buildings require very large space. It is more remarkable still that the compact air-cooling systems designed for railway cars operate so economically that they add little to the cost of traveling.

Throughout the train, as regards interior arrangements, first consideration has been given to comfort and convenience of passengers rather than maximum capacity. In the day car, there are seventeen swivel armchairs with

SOLARIUM   OBSERVATION LOUNGE   WOMEN'S LOUNGE   GENERAL LOUNGE   BUFFET

0   SCALE IN FEET   10

62 · REAR (LOUNGE) CAR NUMBER 4: PLAN   DESIGNED BY NORMAN BEL GEDDES 1931

accommodations for thirty-three persons in all, including those in the smoking lounge.⁶³ The armchairs are semi-upholstered and comfortable, with all parts easily accessible and interchangeable for cleaning and replacement. Entrances, front and rear, are on a diagonal axis. Baggage storage space is provided at each end of the car adjacent to the platform. A rolling steel curtain separates the baggage space from the entrance aisle. Each of the lavatories for men and women has a small entrance foyer with wash basin and wall mirror. There is a roomy smoking lounge for men and women in the center and to one side of the car. This lounge is fitted with two comfortable sofas, two bridge tables, each with four chairs, magazine table, smoking stands and four movable armchairs.

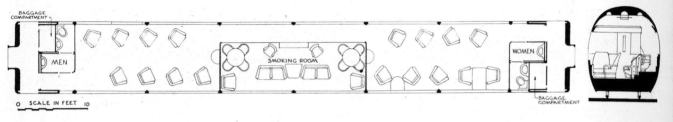

63 · DAY CAR: PLAN & SECTION   DESIGNED BY NORMAN BEL GEDDES 1931

In these cars, in place of the hot radiator running around the base of the walls is a foot rail. The smoking lounge is two steps lower than the floor of the rest of the car. This is made possible because it is situated in the center of the car, where there are no wheel trucks. The ends of the smoking lounge are separated from the rest of the car by a partition of semi-transparent glass that is head height. The ventilating mechanism draws off all smoke immediately. This division of the car approximately into thirds creates the cordiality of the small room in contrast to a long public corridor, with its rows of chairs on each side of the aisle. In the center third of the car the only separation between the aisle and the lounge is a balustrade with an opening in the center leading two steps down into the lounge.

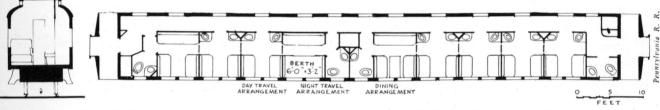

64 · COMPARTMENT CAR   DESIGNED BY PULLMAN COMPANY 1925

In all cars the floors, walls, ceilings, and partitions are insulated for sound. The floor of the day car and all other cars, is of cork, in place of dust-catching carpet, while the walls, from floor to window sill, are finished in lacquer. The trim of the window panes, the railing, and the molding of the partitions, are Monel metal. Tables are of bakelite. Chairs and sofas have removable seats, backs and arms, to facilitate cleaning. They are upholstered in wool tapestry without design or pattern. The upholstery is designed so that it can be easily removed for cleaning after each trip. For summer use, the heavy upholstered

BERTH
6'-0"x3'-2"

DAY TRAVEL ARRANGEMENT   NIGHT TRAVEL ARRANGEMENT   DINING ARRANGEMENT

0   5   10
FEET

65 · COMPARTMENT CAR: PLAN & SECTION   DESIGNED BY PULLMAN COMPANY 1925

chairs and sofas are covered by slip covers. Color schemes vary in different cars to eliminate the standardized appearance.

The night car consists of a series of six large double sleeping rooms (ten feet six inches by six feet eight inches) along one side of the car, and a roomy corridor on the other.[67] Each car is provided with a shower bath, a barber shop, and a porter's pantry for storing glasses, ice, light refreshments. This pantry is equipped so that at night it serves as a small valet's pressing and cleaning room. By day each room comfortably accommodates four persons. There are three large, luxurious easy chairs and one movable side chair. At night, each room accommodates two persons comfortably. These rooms are considerably longer and wider than those in present-day "Drawing Room" cars. In all respects, they are vastly more comfortable.[65]

There are no berths in these rooms, but real three-quarter size beds, six feet five inches long and three feet six inches wide, considerably larger than the Pullman beds. These fold into an easy chair and a sofa during the day.[67]

66 · COMPARTMENT CAR NUMBER 2   DESIGNED BY NORMAN BEL GEDDES 1931

Each room is provided with a large lavatory, as well as a table-desk which drops out of the wall. This can be used as a writing or dining table and for unpacking bags. It is of black bakelite. Over the foot of the bed there is a servidor closet, which opens into the room and at the same time is accessible to the porter from the aisle. Shoes to be polished or suits to be pressed can be taken out or replaced by the porter without disturbing the occupant. Instead

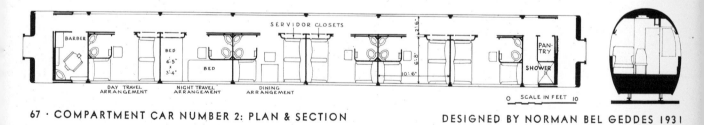

67 · COMPARTMENT CAR NUMBER 2: PLAN & SECTION   DESIGNED BY NORMAN BEL GEDDES 1931

of two windows in the room, each of which is divided vertically and horizontally by a mullion, there is only one. The entire exterior wall is of glass. These windows are seven inches higher at the top than those of the present

Pullman, permitting a passenger standing to look out without stooping. They afford a much greater unobstructed view.

The partitions have simple flat breaks instead of ornamental moldings Armchairs and beds are upholstered in plain wool damask. Side chairs are aluminum with upholstered leather seats. Window shades are of aluminum, on the principle of the Venetian blind. Overhead lights are set into the ceiling and covered flush by frosted glass. For reading, there is a frosted tubing light over the shoulder of each passenger. In the sleeper as in other cars of the train, there can be no draft, as the ventilation is mechanical and the windows are hermetically sealed.

An unbroken view and spacious comfort are the outstanding features of the lounge car.[61] In place of the open-air observation platform,[60] with all its dust and cinders, is the sun room enclosed by sloping glass windows. The sun room, overhanging the rear wheels, is two steps lower than the rest of the car.[62] This lower level of the sun room is dictated by necessity — the tapering form that eliminates vacuum. However, this purely functional feature adds to the comfort of passengers by an increased line of vision.

A buffet, fully equipped with electrical refrigerator, grill, table, soda fountain, cupboards, is at the entrance end of the lounge car.[62] From here, soft drinks and light refreshments can be served throughout the car. Adjacent to the buffet are serving stands. A table for two forms a dining alcove. The general lounge contains built-in bookcases, a radio, telephone, magazine tables, writing desks, and comfortable armchairs, conveniently placed with a wide central aisle. A lavatory opens from the entrance corridor of this car which, like that of the day and night cars, is at the side. A women's lounge is placed across the center of the car. For privacy, it is separated from the main lounge by a six-foot frosted glass partition. A large built-in sofa occupies one end of the women's lounge. Other furnishings include writing desk, five movable armchairs, magazine table and two settees. All chairs and sofas of the lounge car are free standing.

In general, the decorative scheme of this car follows that indicated in connection with the day car. The buffet is built-in, with Monel metal serving counter and bar rail. Serving-tray stands are of Monel metal tubing, supporting a black bakelite top. Passengers will not find it necessary to call a porter for card or writing tables. Pressure on a button in the wall releases a panel which turns up, forming a table.

The entire train is equipped with a telephone system, which has its own switchboard operator. She is also general information clerk for the train. Meals can be ordered without leaving one's room and the dining-room steward can notify the passenger by telephone when a table is available in the dining car. One can talk with passengers in other rooms and in other cars of the train, or make reservations for a bridge table in the lounge or day car.

Throughout the train there are no protruding lighting fixtures. All are set flush within the walls or ceilings, eliminating considerable labor in cleaning as well as chances of breakage. It is my conviction that in the interior decoration of railway cars, the dingy colors — grays, greens and browns now in use — should be avoided. The existing decorative scheme of railway cars suggests that the colors selected are those least likely to show dirt. This should be the last consideration. The cars should be cheerful, gay, inviting; and there should be a touch of personality in furnishings to eliminate the drab atmosphere that exists in present trains.

Many merchandising experts make the mistake of disregarding the tremendous influence of the feminine point of view on sales. They fail to realize that with regard to most purchases, the influence of women is paramount. The majority of men who travel are forced to be away from home by business necessity. On a train, just as in a hotel, they welcome an inviting atmosphere. There is no reason why a railway car should not be as comfortable and as clean as the most up-to-date hotel or ocean liner.

And why should the train of to-day not have a business car? A car that meets the needs of the business man when traveling, as his office meets them when he is at home. The telephone operator is logically located in this car. There will be three private business-office compartments, each equipped with three chairs, a desk, a telephone and a typewriter, which may be used and paid for on an hourly rate. Two public stenographers are available. In addition, standard equipment for this car will include a telephone booth, Trans-lux projection machine for business reports and latest news a safe for papers and valuables, two writing desks, magazine and newspaper service, cigar and cigarette stand, and a telegraph office. The telegraph office obviates the necessity of the hand-to-hand process of dispatching telegrams from trains and eliminates delay. The ticker room has two rows of chairs with an attendant to project bulletins, latest news, quotations. Although in no sense a brokerage office, the ticker room facilities make it possible to telephone or telegraph instructions on the basis of the latest news received. Bridge or other games are not permitted in this car as its purpose is in no sense that of a lounge room.

In general dimensions and design, this car is uniform with the lounge car, day car and night car. It is an application of an idea which has previously been limited to the private cars of captains of industry. If the railroads are to win back the favor of the traveling public, they will probably have to develop in a practical way ideas for the enhanced comfort of passengers in a spacious manner that is *beyond* the possibilities of the motor coach or airplane as the best answer to their competition.

CHAPTER 5

By Air To-morrow

Most present-day airports represent first-thought solutions to problems involved in the housing of planes. From the viewpoint of planes' landing and departing, the movement in and out of passengers, numerous handicaps and inadequacies are inherent, due to the casualness of the basic design. The better class of airports, however, have a semblance of organization in the grouping of the hangars;[68] nevertheless they are not forward looking. Aside from the fact that they are usually remote from the cities they serve and have inadequate means of transportation to and from them, they are adequate for the widely varying uses to which the present-day airport is put.

Owing to the circumstances surrounding aviation development, to-day's airport is usually required to serve a number of different purposes. It furnishes a landing place for transport planes, mail planes, student planes, private planes, sightseeing planes, air meets, experimental and exhibition flying and manufacturing interests as well. Such control as is exercised is that of elementary traffic management.[69] Under the circumstances, the maximum of skill and of familiarity with the particular airport is required of the pilot to

[79]

avoid serious mishaps in landing or taking off. In the future, I believe the several purposes now served by one airport will be separated. Complications will be eliminated by diverting specific forms of flying activities to fields specially adapted to each.

Airways will eventually be one of our main modes of conveyance. With the same progress in the development of equipment in the next ten years as in the past, we can expect the old 5:15 to be a group of ten passenger planes

68 · LAMBERT-ST. LOUIS MUNICIPAL AIRPORT   CHIEF ENGINEER W. W. HORNER 1930

arriving at minute intervals, and which will extend the commuting radius from forty miles to one hundred or one hundred and fifty miles, or more. Since aviation will ultimately occupy as strong a position in the transportation system as the railroads do to-day, airports will require for safe operation the same rigid, standardized control that is now characteristic of our important railway terminals. There will be the same rigid differentiation between freight (comprised of its four main pay loads: freight, express, mail, baggage) and passengers. Every effort will be made to eliminate cross traffic between these two main divisions.

Future developments of flying equipment will eliminate or greatly minimize the number of days lost on account of inclement weather. Still in the infancy of flying, we see the elements as insurmountable. I have no doubt that science will disseminate fog, high winds and other natural phenomena which at present keep the plane on the ground and shake the public's confidence in aviation as a dependable means of transportation; or science will make it possible to fly through them with the same degree of safety as in clear, calm air. Moreover, some means of plane control, which is entirely automatic, will largely eliminate the human element and make flying as safe as railway travel is to-day, with its electric-block-system control. The next few years are bound to bring a new concentrated fuel that will require much less space and have a great deal more energy. Whether or not it will be of a combustible nature is a matter for the chemist.

When these developments occur, flying will not be limited to the adventurous few but will be the logical way to go to and from New York, St. Louis, New Orleans, Los Angeles, Seattle, Chicago, or even between Philadelphia and New York, which are only ninety miles apart. The saving in time is tremendous, the fares nominal, the scenery incomparable, the air clean; hours are reduced to minutes and miles to feet.

Due to the nature of the airplane, which depends

69 · LAMBERT-ST. LOUIS MUNICIPAL AIRPORT: PLAN
CHIEF ENGINEER W. W. HORNER 1930

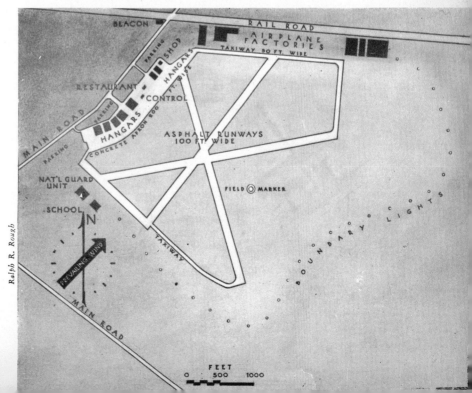

Ralph R. Rough

upon speed for buoyancy, it requires a smooth runway on which to develop sufficient speed to take off and on which to lose speed after landing. Runway distances are shorter now than formerly, due to better plane and motor design, and other devices such as slotted wings and brakes. Shorter runways may be expected in the future, but until the plane is developed which can take off from or land in a restricted area by action similar to that of a helicopter, considerable areas will be required for landing fields. Even autogiro planes, on scheduled flights, must be provided with an adequate and not inconsiderable area in order to land and take off under varying conditions with safety.

This contingency necessitates the removal of the field from the strictly metropolitan areas to adjacent sections where land is less expensive. Thus communication with the city becomes a major problem. If we are not to lose much of the time gained in flight, rapid transit facilities must be provided. But rapid transit facilities to and from airports are provided only when the amount of traffic warrants it. This volume of traffic requires that all but strictly commercial flying be eliminated from the field. When this occurs, the airport will cease to be the center of miscellaneous air activities and become strictly a terminal for air travelers under systematic schedule and control similar to our railroad terminal depots.

Flying equipment, the property of the public carrier, will eventually be manufactured and tested in a plant entirely distinct from the terminal field. Air meets, private planes, sightseeing and student planes, dirigibles, experimental and exhibition flying, will be relegated to other fields. Facilities for mail and express planes, since they come under the head of commercial aviation, must be provided by the air terminal.

To-morrow's transport plane will probably have the capacity of the average railroad car of to-day. If we assume that the number of air passengers in the future will approximate only one tenth the number of rail passengers to-day, the coming air terminal will be confronted with the problem of dispatching a number of planes sufficient to accommodate five hundred passengers (approximately the number carried by a train of ten cars) simultaneously. It is said that a train leaves the Pennsylvania Railroad Station in New York every minute. Obviously, with their present facilities, no airport could load and dispatch planes on any such schedule with equal efficiency and ease to-day. Most airports have but one loading point to which all outgoing planes taxi to receive their passengers. A schedule of a plane a minute would mean that a plane would have to taxi up, load fifty passengers and their baggage, taxi out and take off all in one minute — a physical impossibility under present arrangements.

It is essential that passengers be kept isolated from the whirling propellers while the plane is standing or idling, as the blades are practically invisible and to be struck by them means instant death. The control of passengers in present-day airports in this respect is dependent upon the alert supervision of the field attendants. This responsibility is handled in an informal way which lessens rather than enhances that feeling of security and safety so evident in present-day railway travel and so essential to air travel.

The seeming haphazard nature of present-day airport operations, in contrast with the dignity and solidity manifest in the architecture and operating methods of railroads, is one of the handicaps commercial aviation must overcome before the confidence of the public in air transportation can be fully established. To-day, the confusion is such that passengers from an arriving plane find themselves mingling and jostling with baggagemen, postal employees, mechanics, guards, and pilots. In connection with the casualness of to-day's airport facilities may also be noted the lack of provision for loading and unloading planes in inclement weather.

In the air terminal I have designed, I have, I believe, overcome the major airport conditions that are subject to criticism. I have taken advantage of the fact that we are free to look ahead and plan for impending developments. As the object of the design is to eliminate shortcomings that exist in connection with airports to-day, while providing for the future, the primary objectives, when stated, appear as the reverse of the criticisms already noted. For reasons already indicated, I have excluded from this terminal all aërial activity except the scheduled transportation of passengers and the handling of mail and express by heavier-than-air craft. Both aërial and vehicular traffic are accommodated with safety and flexibility and without confusion.

The Air Terminal is approximately one mile square.[70] The Lambert-St. Louis Municipal Airport[68] occupies approximately nine tenths of a square mile.

It consists of a landing field thirty-six hundred feet square, with a hard, smooth, dustless surface, which does not become soggy or slippery when wet, and can be readily cleared of snow. On four sides it is surrounded by repair and storage hangars, mail, express, and passenger slips. These, to the limit of the airport property, at least eight hundred feet in each direction, definitely control the height of obstructions. There are no landing strips as the field is an " all way " field, suitable for landing or taking off into the wind from any direction.[75] Surrounding the field is a taxi strip of concrete four hundred feet wide.[71-P] On this planes taxi to their unloading slips or from their loading slips to their take-off position.[71-Q] The entire field is used exclusively for taking off or landing, and all planes must taxi to the surrounding strip before changing direction.

Illuminated boundary markers, which are set around the inside edge of the taxi strip, raised slightly above the field and hooded for proper visibility in the manner of traffic lights, mark the limit of the landing field.[74] Red and green lights designating the safe landing and take-off area are automatically

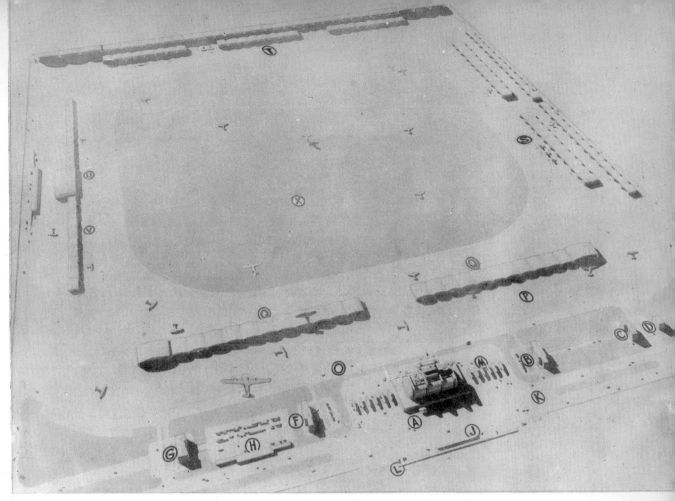

controlled by the illuminated wind tee, located in the center of an illuminated circle at the center of the field, to enable the landing pilot to determine the limits of the safe landing area and the direction of the wind. Horizontal traffic is controlled by red and green lights, hooded, so as to be visible in a horizontal direction only and are controlled from the wind tee and the control bridge."[73-N]

This system contemplates that all traffic shall move in a counter clockwise direction around the field, the take-off area showing red to the air and the landing area showing green. In case of difficulty in any part of the field, the whole system can be switched red as a signal for all planes on the ground to stop and all planes in the air to remain aloft.

Flood lights are placed on all four sides of the field and are controlled by

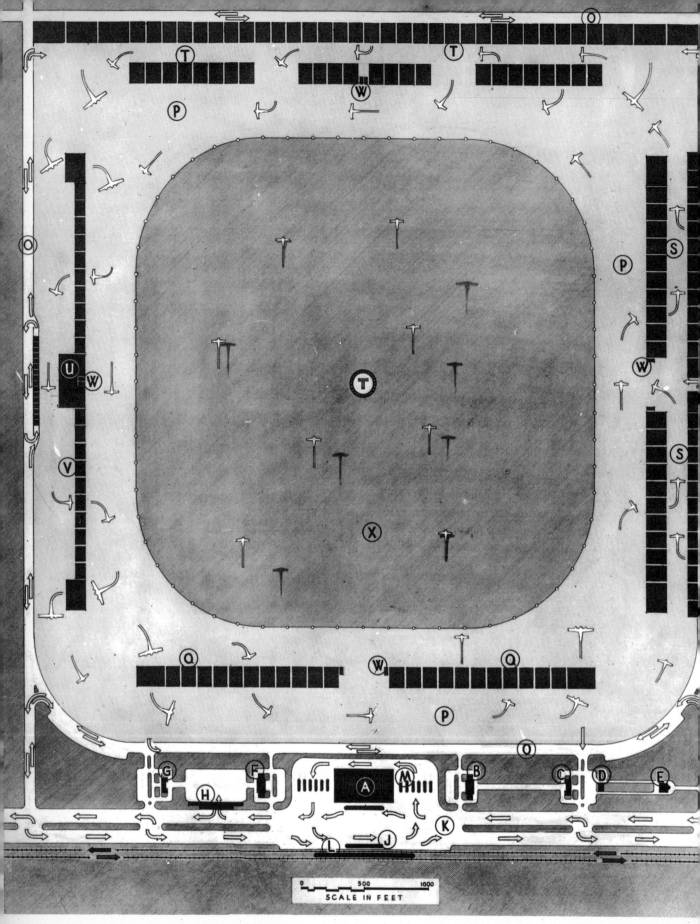

71 · AIR TERMINAL: GROUND LEVEL TRAFFIC DIAGRAM   DESIGNED BY NORMAN BEL GEDDES 1932

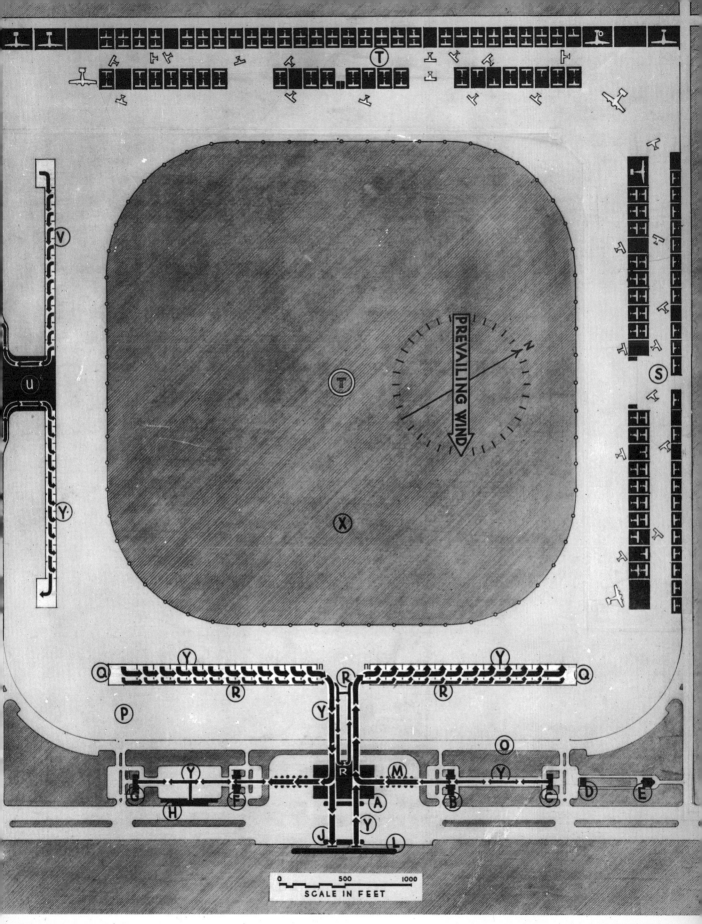

PREVAILING WIND

SCALE IN FEET
0   500   1000

72 · AIR TERMINAL: UNDERGROUND TRAFFIC DIAGRAM   DESIGNED BY NORMAN BEL GEDDES 1932

the wind tee, to furnish illumination from the side rather than directly ahead or behind the incoming or outgoing planes. The flood lights, spaced about one hundred and twenty-five feet apart, are placed on the hangars which surround the field. They are focussed so as to confine the rays of light to a height of six feet. Each bank of flood lights has sufficient power to illuminate the entire width of the field. Thus, planes or other objects on the field are readily visible from all directions and no elongated shadows are thrown on the field. In the event of the failure of any flood-light unit, there still is sufficient illumination for safely landing and taking-off.

The control bridge,[73-N] including the radio, meteorological offices, and traffic control office, is located above the roof terrace, on the field side of the terminal building.[73-A] This position gives a clear view of the entire field. A ceiling projector and revolving beacon are located at the tops of the two towers which project above the control bridge.

The height of all buildings facing the field is less than one seventh the width of the taxi strip. Flood lighting of the facades and of all structures adjacent to the field to the same intensity as the field reduces glare and permits the pilot to maintain his perspective and judgment of distance. Electricity for illumination and power in the various departments of the port is generated at a centrally located power house[71-E] and distributed underground from a transformer station[71-D] located between the repair shops and terminal building. All flood lighting is controlled by a photoëlectric system which automatically maintains a constant intensity.

A hospital[71-C] is adjacent to the flying field. Four fire stations and ambulance stations[71-W] are located on the cross axis of the field in the mail and express depot and between the two groups of repair hangars. This distribution permits of rapid aid in an emergency. An eighty-foot automobile road[71-O] completely surrounds the field, so that in case of accident ambulances can reach the hospital[71-C] without the necessity of disrupting traffic on the field or taxi strips.

To the right of the field, viewed from the terminal building, are located the repair hangars.[72-S] Here, 64 planes of 110 feet wing spread, and 2 of 210 feet wing spread can simultaneously undergo incidental repairs or major overhauling. These hangars are so arranged that when repairs are complete any plane can be removed without disturbing any other plane. It can then taxi under its own power to the storage hangars on the opposite side of the field from the terminal.[72-T] The storage hangars provide facilities for storing 120 planes of 110 feet wing spread and 6 planes having a spread of 210 feet. Here also, out of the weather and free from tampering, are housed planes held in reserve for rush periods. Each plane is easily accessible at all times.

Incoming and outgoing slips for express and mail planes[71-V] are across the field from the repair hangars. Incoming planes land into the wind and proceed directly into the incoming slips from the taxi strip. Each incoming plane is assigned, by a system of lights and semaphores, to a particular slip into which it taxies and comes to rest, facing the circulation space behind. Mail or express from these planes is conveyed by underground tunnels to the depot located midway between the incoming and outgoing slips.[72-U]

Facilities for fueling and minor servicing are provided in both the incoming and outgoing slips.[71-Q] The plane crew looks after this routine while loading or unloading is in progress.[74] The express or freight plane making only a transient stop loses no time in refueling. Separation of the air express, freight and mail planes from the passenger traffic eliminates the confusion incident to handling them together and permits better supervision and control over mail shipments.

It is the opinion of some air transport companies, which at present carry

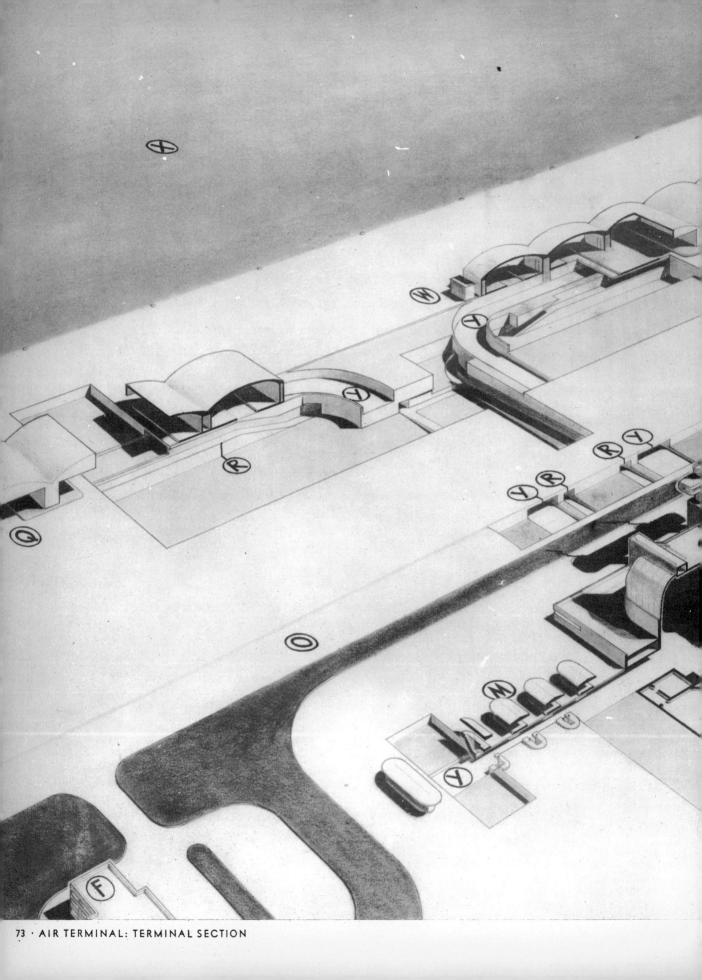

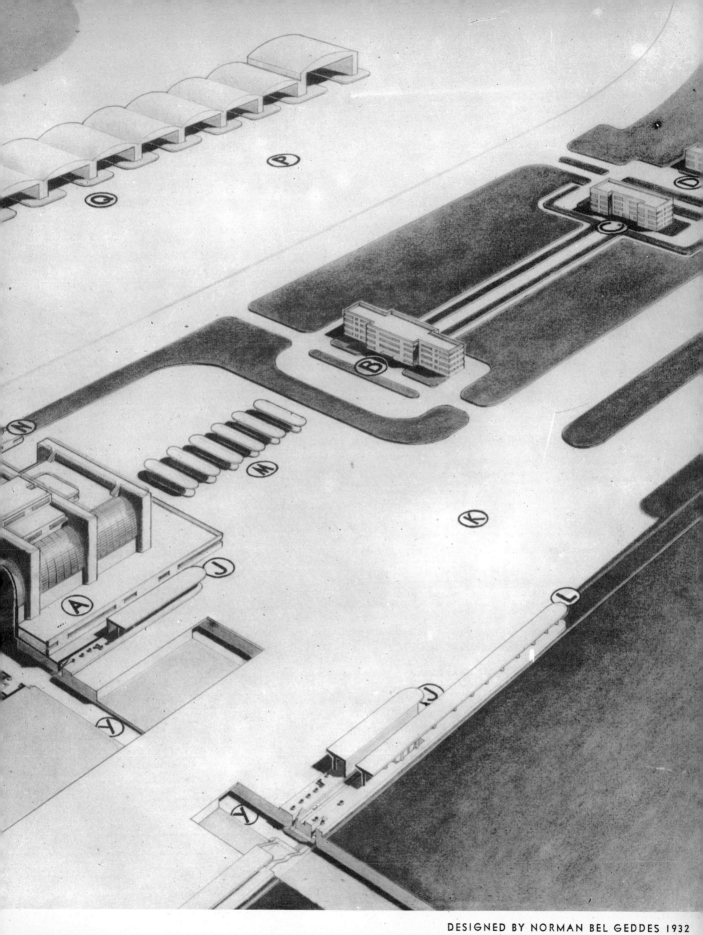

DESIGNED BY NORMAN BEL GEDDES 1932

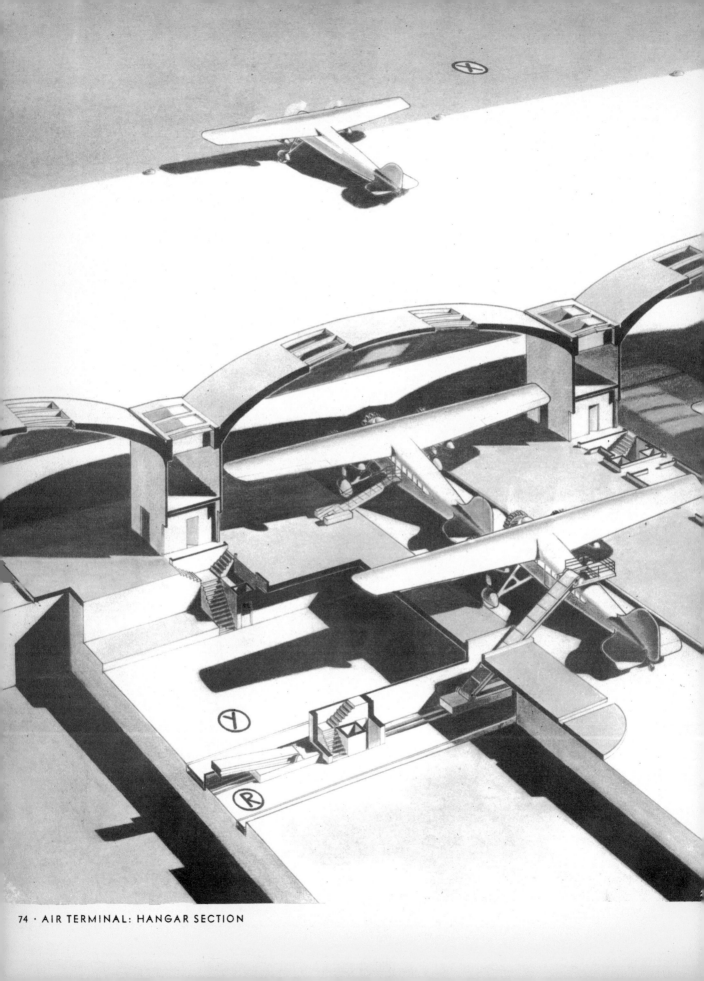

DESIGNED BY NORMAN BEL GEDDES 1932

both express and mail in the same planes with passengers, that these services will not be entirely separated. Until the volume of both mail and passenger traffic warrants it, such a division will, of course, not be economical. It is reasonable to assume that in the future, as facilities for the safe and scheduled transport of mail are developed, the bulk of all interstate mail will be carried by plane. Hence we have set aside four incoming and four outgoing slips adjacent to the express depot for the exclusive use of mail planes. In this building, we have allotted sufficient space for sorting and distributing the mail. One starting slip adjacent to the eleven passenger slips is reserved for the exclusive use of mail and express planes, so that their movements come under the same single control as all other traffic on this field.

The passenger terminal[71-A] is located at the side of the field adjacent to the main highway[71-K] and the rapid transit electric lines.[71-L] The circulation of motor-car transportation in connection with the terminal is so arranged that taxis,[71-M] buses,[71-J] and private cars[71-M] travel, in the congested areas, in only one direction. Where cross traffic is necessary, generous curves and clearances are provided to permit the rapid movement of traffic in every direction. Major provision for vehicular and rapid transit traffic has been made on the assumption that pedestrian traffic will be negligible, since the field is located at some distance from the metropolitan center. In this respect, the air terminal differs from a railroad terminal, in connection with which, owing to its bulk, pedestrian traffic is of primary importance.

The terminal has four covered platforms at which incoming taxis discharge their passengers.[73-M] Two additional platforms are provided for private automobiles. At each of these platforms eight cars may unload simultaneous-

ly. These platforms are connected with the outgoing side of the terminal by moving walks in an underground passage.[72-Y] Two loading platforms three hundred feet in length are provided for buses in front of the terminal building on either side of the main highway.[73-J] These platforms are also connected with the terminal by moving walks in underground passages[73-Y] which also extend to the railroad and subway lines.[72-L] From the bus and railroad tunnels one enters directly into the main concourse of the terminal building,[73-Y] which is three hundred and fifty feet in length by one hundred and fifty in width, with a ceiling height of eighty feet. The moving sidewalk deposits the passenger at the entrance to the tunnel for outgoing planes. To the right are located the outgoing waiting room, merchandise shops, the tunnel from the incoming taxi platform, hospital, telephone and telegraph booths. To the left are the ticket offices and outgoing baggage room.[72-R]

Passengers about to embark present their tickets at the entrance of the outgoing tunnel where, at the proper time, they are conveyed by a moving walk to the slip in which their plane is berthed.[73-Q] Upon showing their ticket, they take an elevator to the ground level and board the plane by means of a cantilevered gangway[74] which is adjustable to any size or type of plane. This system provides a double control: it prevents passengers from boarding wrong planes and eliminates the danger of their entering a plane while it is in motion. There are ten passenger slips accommodating planes up to 110 feet wing spread and one accommodating planes up to 210 feet. An outgoing plane taxies into the baggage side of an outgoing slip (from its previous position in an incoming slip or a storage hangar) upon signal from the control tower. Here it is loaded with baggage by means of a mechanical conveyor,[74-R]

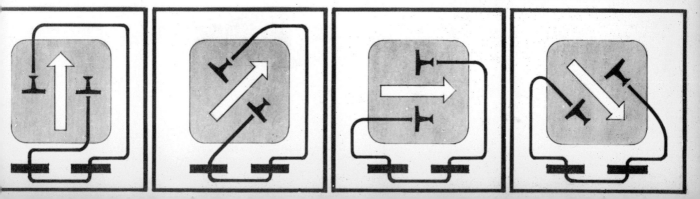

fueled and given final inspection simultaneously, the whole operation to b completed within ten minutes.

A preliminary inspection had previously been given on the baggage side of the incoming slip to determine the extent of service needed. A final inspection is given on the baggage side of the outgoing slip. After the final inspector's approval is given, a rolling metal door[74-Z] separating the baggage from the passenger side of the slip is raised, permitting the plane to taxi into a position where passengers may board it, and the next plane taxies into the baggage side.[74-Q] Passengers are not permitted to enter the loading slip until the plane and the gangplank are in position. Then the gates at the tunnel level are opened and passengers board the plane in a clean, dry, heated enclosure.

At the expiration of its ten-minute loading time, the gate is closed, the hangar doors are opened, the plane taxies out onto the strip adjacent to the field and from there to its take-off position. Planes are scheduled to leave each slip every ten minutes. Thus, using ten or twelve outgoing slips, a plane a minute may be dispatched in a most orderly fashion with ample time for servicing (or replacement by another plane) and loading of baggage and passengers.

Arriving at the terminal by plane, the passenger debarks in a covered slip[71-Q] and proceeds by stairs or elevators to the tunnel level where he rides on the moving walk to the terminal building.[72-Y] Here he proceeds without interruption to the taxi,[73-M] or to the bus,[73-J] or railway tunnel.[73-L] An incoming waiting room with telephone, telegraph and radio facilities is located conveniently between them. Information booth and ticket desks are in the center of the concourse.

While the passenger is on his way through the passenger tunnel, his baggage has been unloaded from the plane and transported to the underground baggage room, which is located between the incoming and outgoing tun-

Fairchild Aërial Surveys, Inc.

76 · ROTARY AIRPORT: AIRPLANE VIEW   DESIGNED BY NORMAN BEL GEDDES 1930

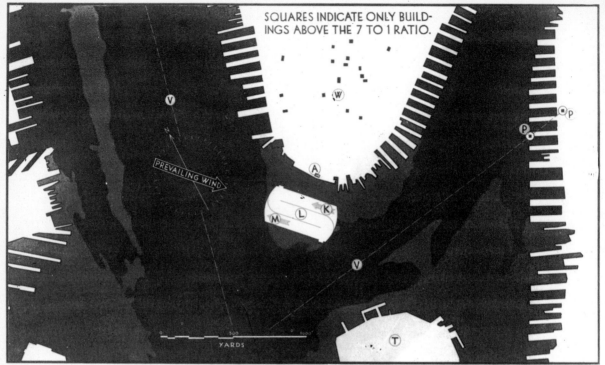

PREVAILING WIND

77 · ROTARY AIRPORT: HARBOR PLAN   DESIGNED BY NORMAN BEL GEDDES 1930

nels[72-R] in the terminal building. Here it is checked out or other disposition arranged for. If his baggage is subject to customs, he enters the customs inspection room from the main concourse. Baggage is issued directly into this space from the baggage room.

All immigration facilities, including a waiting room, medical examination and public health offices, travelers' aid booth, and other departments incidental to this government function are provided.

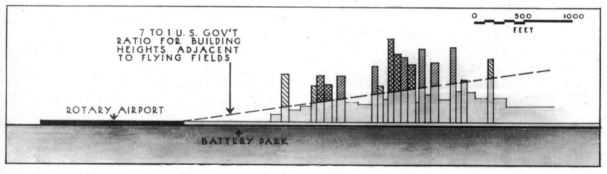

7 TO 1 U. S. GOV'T
RATIO FOR BUILDING
HEIGHTS ADJACENT
TO FLYING FIELDS

ROTARY AIRPORT

BATTERY PARK

78 · ROTARY AIRPORT: CLEARANCE DIAGRAM OF TALL BUILDINGS (SIDE ELEVATION)

Restaurant and quick-lunch bars are located on the concourse level. Those who wish to dine more leisurely, or to celebrate the arrival or departure of friends, find a large restaurant, with salon and ample observation pavilions over the main concourse.[73-A] It is reached by elevators from the concourse level.

The underground moving-walk system joins the terminal with the office building,[72-B] the hotel,[72-F] the garage and automobile parking area,[72-H] the pilots' club[72-G] and the hospital.[72-C]

Air terminals of this nature, with refinements and conveniences exceeding those indicated will, I believe, be a feature of our principal cities within ten years. Eventually every large city that is now an important rail center — excluding those which are strictly freight centers — will be obliged to organize air-terminal facilities more or less in the manner indicated and approximately on the same scale. The outstanding feature of this project is that it looks ahead. The plan can be developed by stages, as every airport should be. The main requisite is for sufficient thoroughness in terms of to-morrow's developments, so that displacement of buildings will be unnecessary.

AIR TERMINAL

A. Terminal Building	G. Pilot's Club	P. 400' Taxi Strip	V. Baggage & Mail
B. Office Building	H. Garage & Parking	Q. Take Off &	Hangar
C. Hospital	J. Bus	Landing Slips	W. Fire and Ambu-
D. Transformer	K. Main Highway	R. Baggage Tunnel	lance Station
Station	L. Rapid Transit Line	S. Repair Hangars	X. Flying Area
E. Power House	M. Taxi	T. Storage Hangars	Y. Passenger Terminal
F. Hotel	N. Control Bridge	U. Baggage & Mail	Z. Metal Door
	O. 80' Boundary Road	Depot	

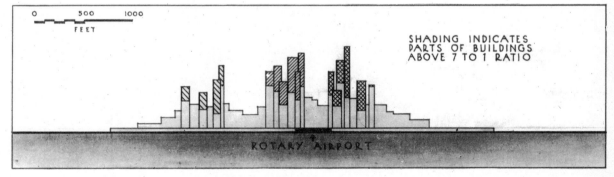

0   500   1000
FEET

SHADING INDICATES PARTS OF BUILDINGS ABOVE 7 TO 1 RATIO

ROTARY AIRPORT

79 · ROTARY AIRPORT: CLEARANCE DIAGRAM OF TALL BUILDINGS (FRONT ELEVATION)

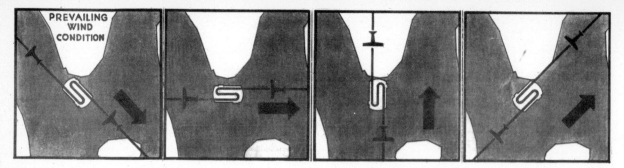

ROTARY AIRPORT

A. Tunnel Entrance Building
B. Shuttle Tunnel
C. Suspended Passenger Tunnel
D. Deck Pinion
E. Elevator
F. Tide Compensating Platform
G. Terminal Hall
H. Departing Station
J. Arriving Station
K. Landing Strip
L. Taxi Strip
M. Take Off Strip
N. Boundary Light
P. Beacons
Q. Wind Indicator
R. Buoyancy Tanks
S. Battery Park
T. Governor's Island
V. Center of Channel
W. Manhattan

Another idea in airports, that is much more specialized, is exemplified by the Rotary Airport designed especially for New York City.

To merely suggest the idea of locating a floating airport anywhere in the navigable portions of New York Harbor, with its tugs, lighters, barges, ferries and sight-seeing boats, brings endless protest from the owners and operators of these harbor craft. Nevertheless this location is ideal for such an airport in terms of proximity to the financial center, unobstructed landing area, relatively stable and uniform winds, excellent land transportation facilities, and lack of interference with vessels of deep draft.

Southwest of Battery Park,[76-8] between the Aquarium and the Staten Island

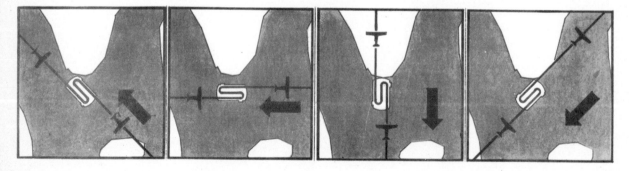

Ferry slips, is an area of water having an average depth at low tide of about twenty-six feet which, while adequate for the small harbor craft, is too shallow for the deeper draft vessels such as liners and warships. This area is large enough to permit a floating landing strip, equal in area to seven New York City blocks, to turn on a pivot located at its approximate center without

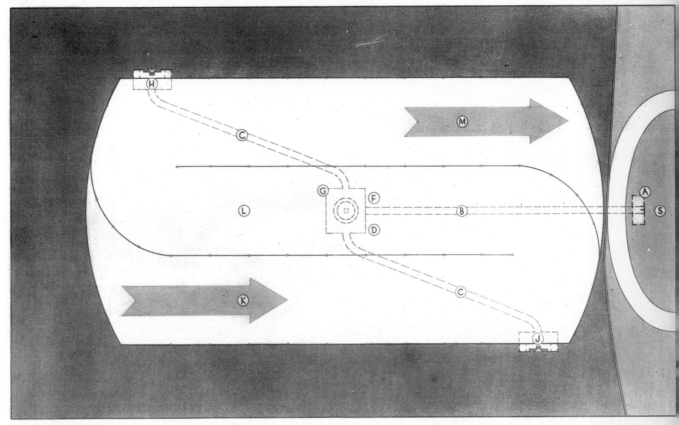

81 · ROTARY AIRPORT: TRAFFIC DIAGRAM   DESIGNED BY NORMAN BEL GEDDES 1930

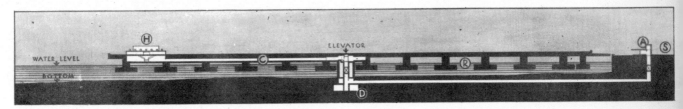

82 · ROTARY AIRPORT: LONGITUDINAL SECTION   DESIGNED BY NORMAN BEL GEDDES 1930

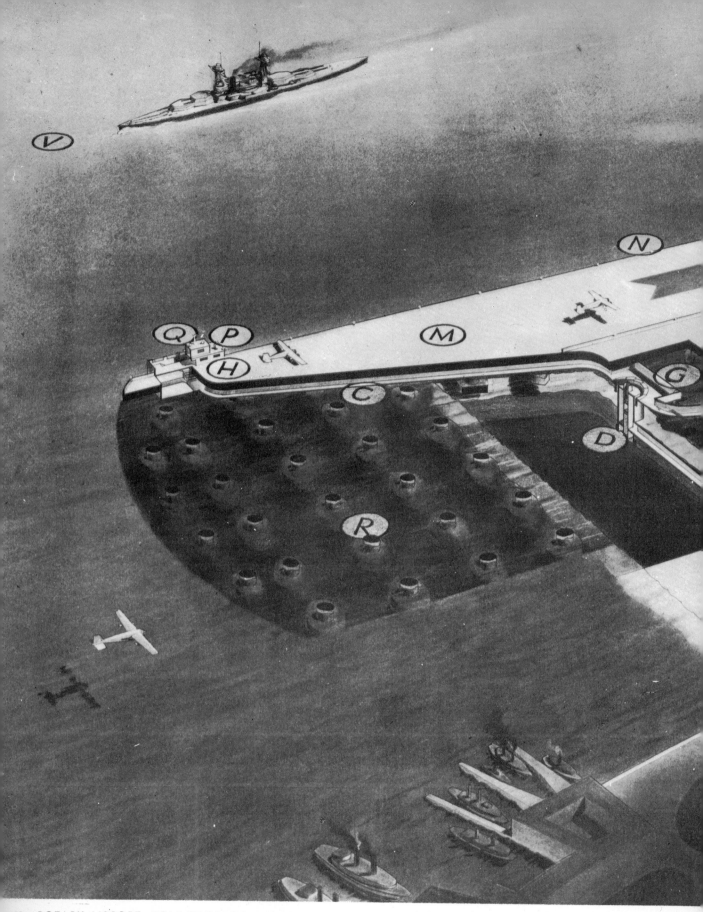

DESIGNED BY NORMAN BEL GEDDES 1930

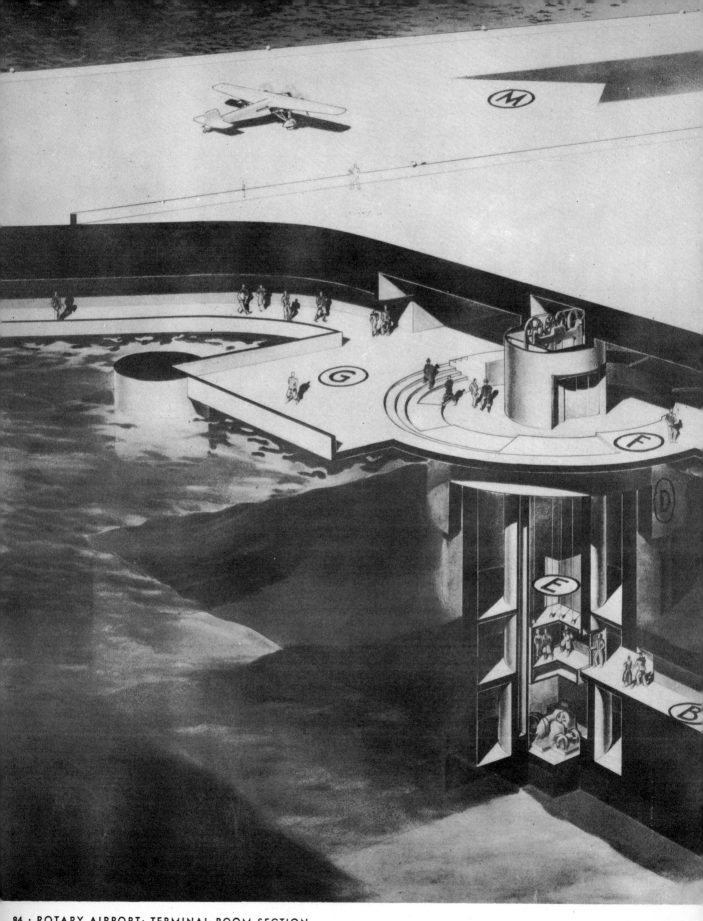

84 · ROTARY AIRPORT: TERMINAL ROOM SECTION

DESIGNED BY NORMAN BEL GEDDES 1930

projecting into either the North River channel[77-V] or the channel between Governor's Island[77-T] and the Battery. The battleship in illustration Number 83 is exactly in the center of the channel, while the liner is in the conventional path taken by ships leaving the North River. This illustrates the ample clearances which are possible with the landing deck in its prevailing wind position.

When aviation assumes the important position in our transportation system which it is destined to occupy, the necessity for adequate and convenient airport facilities immediately accessible to New York's business districts[77-W] will offset to a large degree the objections which now confront the idea of an airport adjacent to the Battery.

The worst condition of the port is when the wind is sweeping down Manhattan towards the deck, a condition which rarely exists.[80] Even then, when planes have to rise over the building towers, we find very few towers projecting above the seven to one ratio[78,79] which the Department of Commerce has determined as the angle of safe glide and rise; and those which do fortunately group themselves to form definite lanes with large clearances over the greatest wing spreads.

As a possible solution to the airport problem New York City will ultimately face, I have designed this floating airport for the accommodation of land planes. It is a large deck fifteen hundred feet long by seven hundred and fifty feet wide and consists of a continuous strip twice doubling back upon itself to make three spaces separated by three-foot curbs. The traffic through these strips is one of continuous motion. One strip is for landing,[81-K] the middle one is a taxi strip,[81-L] and the third is a take-off strip.[81-M] On the top of the dividing wall are mounted green and red boundary lights[84-N] visible from the air, while the entire deck is flooded with light from the two passenger shelters located at the end of the landing strip and at the start of the take-off strip.[81-H]

Mounted on the roofs of these shelters are the identification beacons and fog-penetrating signals.[83-P]

Passengers, arriving by plane, taxi to the end of the incoming strip,[76-K] where they debark into a low shelter,[83-J] from which stairs lead down to the incoming waiting room located beneath the deck. A suspended passenger tunnel[84-C] leads from this waiting room to the terminal hall[84-G] situated at the center of the structure surrounding the deck pinion.[83-D] This space consists of a hollow reinforced concrete cylinder fifty feet in diameter, containing a passenger elevator[84-E] giving direct access to the shuttle tunnel.[84-B] The tunnel is fifteen feet below the bottom of the harbor and eight hundred feet long. It has a moving walk to take passengers ashore to the tunnel entrance building,[83-A] which connects with the street level by elevator where passengers may take taxi, surface car, elevated, or subway.

Times Wide World

85 · ORIGINAL BIPLANE   DESIGNED BY WILBUR & ORVILLE WRIGHT 1903

The weight of this floating airport is supported by columns upon ballasted buoyancy tanks.[83-R] These tanks, located below the portion of the water disturbed by surface waves, keep the deck level in all weather, the waves passing easily around the columns and under the bottom of the deck structure. The landing deck rotates with the wind to give ideal landing and take-off facilities. This rotation is accomplished by motor-driven marine propellers located at the extremities of the long axis of the deck below the water surface. Inasmuch as the starting switches of these propeller-motors are controlled by

a remote wind-indicator,[83-Q] they are fully automatic. The deck with its defi-nite traffic lanes is constantly held in the best position and there is no con-fusion to landing planes. To facilitate the easy rotation of the deck, the float tanks[83-R] are streamlined.

Provision is made for the four-foot tide fluctuation by making the top of the pivot[83-D] the elevator landing, which appears as a stationary disc in the center of the terminal hall.[84-G] As the level of the terminal hall fluctuates with the tide, the passengers reach the stationary landing by means of a tide-compensating platform.[84-F] This platform is a series of circular steps concen-tric about the elevator.[84-E] The various levels of the steps compensate the changing heights of the tide. Beneath the center taxi strip are tanks for refueling planes. The airport, however, is essentially a transient port and re-fueling and repair work are services offered only in an emergency and at an increased price.

Aviation, the world over, is progressing almost entirely on a purely mili-

tary basis. Government coöperation is from this standpoint and is the outstanding handicap in the development of commercial aviation. With the expansion of aviation from the commercial standpoint security, economy and comfort, which are the principal factors from the public's standpoint, will develop to a point now unthought of.

More people have been accused of being fools regarding aviation than for any other reason within our time. Both of the Wright brothers were spoken of as such. In 1910 the State of Missouri nearly passed a bill making any aviator who flew at an elevation of one thousand or more feet guilty of attempted suicide. In 1912 Captain Nestereff, a military engineer of the Russian Imperial Air Force, made the first loop in a plane, after having carefully figured it out on paper.

88 · DO-X: INTERIOR   DESIGNED BY CLAUDE DORNIER 1929

He did it for no other reason than as a scientific experiment in which he believed to the extent of risking his own life. Upon his landing, superior officers placed him under arrest and he was courtmartialed. The charge was that an officer of the Russian Army should not foolishly risk his life but should save it for his country in time of war. Captain Nestereff was killed in action in 1914.

For a number of years I have been working on plans for a big plane. It is not " big " for the sake of being big but for other factors which will be apparent as I describe it. It is my firm belief that this is in no sense a mad or fool-

ish idea but sound in every particular. It represents my idea of what the intercontinental air liner of 1940 will be like.

The plane that the Wright brothers flew at Kitty Hawk a few years back was little more than a box kite.[35] Compare the earliest biplanes with to-day's of the comparatively same wing spread, and there is one noticeable difference — weight. The ratio in size and bulk of the wings, fuselage and motor has changed considerably.[19] This difference will be still further accentuated as intercontinental aviation develops. Ships, railways, and automobiles have developed similarly. Size will provide safety, and space (which is size) will make travel by airplane as comfortable as travel by steamship.

The largest heavier-than-air craft built and successfully flown to date is the DO-X.[36] She has a wing spread of 157 feet, a length of 131 feet, a height of 33 feet, and her normal weight in flight is 48 tons. The ship is 3 decks high,[87] and although she has successfully carried more than 150 people at

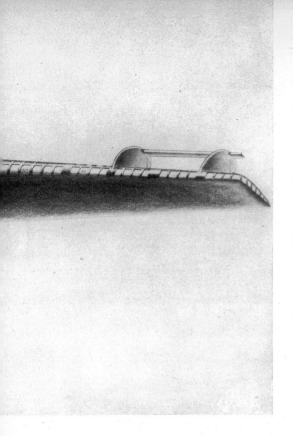

one time, this is several times her capacity in terms of sleeping space and comfort."[88] Considerable progress in aërodynamics has been made since Doctor Dornier built her, with the result that the next airship as large or larger will be a great improvement over the DO-X.

As a premise, one must accept the fact that the air liner I am going to describe will fly, and fly just as readily as any other plane. In fact, I have every reason to believe that it will fly much more smoothly than any plane that has yet been built, if for no other reason than because of its enormous size.

In this undertaking I have associated with me Doctor O. A. Koller, as aëronautical engineer. Doctor Koller is responsible for the design of over two hundred different airplanes, including the famous Phalz plane used so extensively by Germany during the World War. His fourteen years' association with the aëroplane industry include three and one half years with the German Government as chief engineer in charge of design and construction of airplanes for both the army and navy. He has developed very favorable airfoils for wings and pontoons; streamlines for fuselage; and without exception, all of his planes have flown successfully.

Air Liner Number 4 is a tailless " V "-winged monoplane, carrying (sleeping accommodations) a total of 606 persons — 451 passengers and a crew of 155. She has a total wing spread of 528 feet.[89] On the water she is supported by 2 pontoons 104 feet apart, 235 feet long and 60 feet high.[90] Better to visualize the size of this plane, imagine that if it were possible to stand her upon one wing tip against the Washington Monument,[4] she would lack only 23 feet of reaching the top. Or imagine that the Public Library was removed from its site in Bryant Park at Forty-second Street and Fifth Avenue, New York. The plane could then settle comfortably in the park with a clearance of about 35 feet all around.

The "V" of the wing encloses an angle of approximately 120° on the leading edge and 140° on the trailing edge. The wings taper from a chord width of 123 feet at the pontoon to 78 feet at the tip.[96] In thickness, the wing varies from 10 feet 6 inches at the tip to 22 feet at the center.[91] The auxiliary wing[89] located above the main wing is 180 feet in length by 54 feet in width — 23 feet longer than the main wing of the DO-X.[86] Other details of outstanding interest are as follows: Total power required, 38,000 horse power — 20 motors, each 1,900 horse power; maximum speed, 150 miles per hour; cruising speed, 100 miles per hour; landing speed, 72 miles per hour; normal flying altitude, 5,000 feet; absolute ceiling, 10,000 feet; time of climb to ceiling, 1 hour; speed at ceiling, 87½ miles per hour; cruising range without refueling, 7,500 miles; gross weight, 1,275,300 pounds; dead load, 662,600 pounds, which includes wings, pontoons, motors, tanks and fixed equipment; live load, 612,700 pounds, which includes fuel, passengers, crew, baggage, mail supplies and movable furnishings.

90 · AIR LINER NUMBER 4

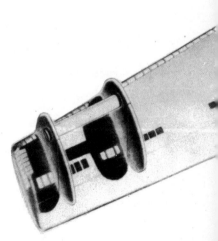

Originally, certain Chicago business men were interested in the possibility of constructing this plane with the idea of operating it between Chicago and London via the St. Lawrence River and Great Circle Route. Careful figures based on a detailed study of all factors involved indicate that the venture is practicable from a commercial viewpoint. The flying time of this plane between Chicago and Plymouth is forty-two hours. She is refueled in flight while passing over Newfoundland. She is able to make three crossings a week, due allowance being made for overhauling in port. This is a great advantage in competition with ocean liners, the fastest of which can make only one crossing a week.

The cost of building, equipping and furnishing a modern ocean liner approximates $60,000,000. Air Liner Number 4 can be built, equipped, and

DESIGNED BY NORMAN BEL GEDDES 1929
AERONAUTICAL ENGINEER OTTO KOLLER

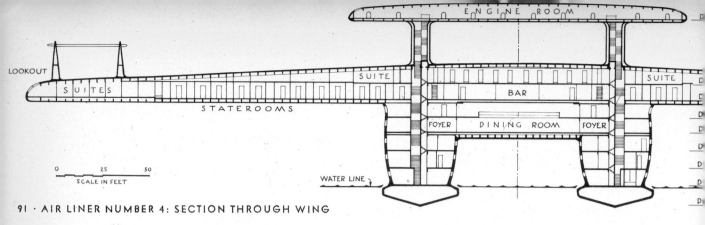

furnished for approximately $9,000,000. Assume that after the air liner has made half a dozen successful round trips on schedule, she will thereafter be filled to capacity. Further, assume that the price per passenger will be the same as an average first-class steamship passage, say $300. Furthermore, realize that the accommodations of this air liner are equal in spaciousness and comfort to the most modern ocean liner. The revenue per trip from fares will then be $135,300 and for the three trips a week, $405,000. Mail $48,000 and baggage $17,000, giving a weekly gross revenue of $470,900. The cost of crew wages for the week will approximate $8,000; fuel and maintenance $121,500; supplies, food and other items, $10,000. Insurance, office rent, salaries and overhead $76,750; depreciation on plane based on only a three-year life, $57,700, which totals a weekly operating expense of $273,950. This shows a net weekly revenue of $196,950. The plane, therefore, returns 10 per cent on the investment and amortizes its cost in approximately three years, whereas, owing to greater original cost and higher operating expense, the modern ocean liner cannot pay for herself in many, many times this period.

The plane carries twenty-six 1900 horse-power motors. Twenty of these are mounted in the auxiliary wing.[91] The interior of this auxiliary wing is a thoroughly equipped engine room, with machine and repair shops, and carries the other six motors in reserve.[97] All motors are mounted on wheel carriages, on tracks, so as to be interchangeable in flight, and easily moved from one location to another within the wing, when disconnected from the pro-

DESIGNED BY NORMAN BEL GEDDES 1929
AERONAUTICAL ENGINEER OTTO KOLLER

peller. By this arrangement it is possible to replace any disabled motor with a reserve motor within five minutes. The disabled motor is run over to the machine shop where it can be immediately repaired.

In spite of the immense size of the plane, it has not been necessary to depart from well-established principles in connection with the control mechanism. In this design the lateral control surfaces are located on top of the main wing near the tips. They appear as two large fins, twenty feet in height and thirty-five feet apart.[90] Rudders are hinged by means of a knuckle joint to continue the streamline of the stabilizer and reduce air resistance. Ailerons for the vertical control and banking of the ship are located in the trailing edge of the main wing.[90] They operate much after the fashion of similar mechanisms on conventional airplanes. All control surfaces are balanced to reduce the effort required to operate them.

In the design of this plane, two major elements have had foremost consideration: first, safety; second, comfort of passengers. Both of these factors have been solved mainly by her immense size. As regards the safety factor, it has been possible to make elaborate provision. While twenty 1900 horsepower motors are required to raise her from the water, twelve are sufficient to fly her at cruising speed. Thus, counting the six reserve motors, she is equipped with more than twice as many motors as will be necessary after once

92 · AIR LINER NUMBER 4: SECTION THROUGH FUSILAGE

DESIGNED BY NORMAN BEL GEDDES 1929
AERONAUTICAL ENGINEER OTTO KOLLER

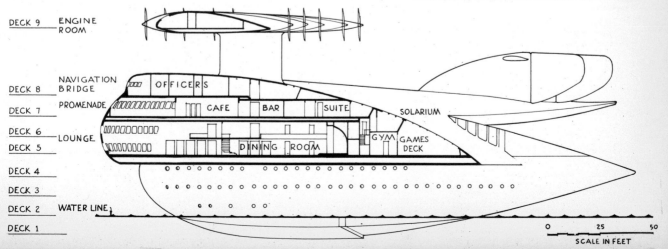

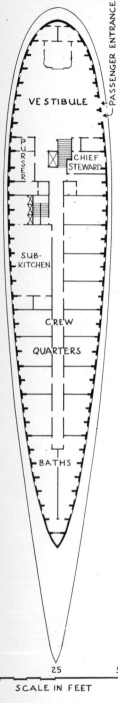

rising from the water — a safety factor of over one hundred per cent.

The pontoons, in construction, are designed substantially as the hull of a yacht, in order to withstand tremendous pounding when the plane rests on a rough sea.[89] In each pontoon are three lifeboats.[94] They are forty feet long, accommodate one hundred and ten persons each, are entirely enclosed, have windows along the side, are motor driven, equipped with sending and receiving radio apparatus, food, and water for two weeks. The capacity of the six boats more than accommodates the total number of passengers and crew. In addition, the liner carries two small auxiliary seaplanes with folding wings, which can be launched in flight or at rest.[95] The primary use for the seaplane is to bring assistance in an emergency.

Over all, the plane as designed is nine decks high.[91] Four of these decks are in the pontoons. The pontoon decks are in pairs. Decks 1 L and 1 R, for instance, are on the same level in the left-hand and right-hand pontoons respectively. These decks are in the bottoms of the hulls. They carry the storage tanks from which fuel is pumped to service tanks in the auxiliary wing. Decks 2 L and 2 R are immediately above Decks 1 L and 1 R. Half the space on these decks is required for fuel and the remainder is devoted to pumps and storage for baggage.

Deck 3 L, in the left pontoon, provides the baggage entrance, sorting space, mechanical baggage conveyors and the baggage master's office. The rear part of this deck is occupied by crew's quarters. Deck 3 R [93] provides an entrance vestibule for passengers, with information desk and various offices and suites of the Chief Purser, Chief Stewards and personnel. An auxiliary kitchen for room service is located on this deck and the remaining space is used for additional quarters for the crew.

Forward, on Decks 4 L [94] and 4 R, are the lookout stations. Immediately back of them are staterooms. The middle portion of Deck 4 L has the main kitchen, with its pantry, refrigerator and supply rooms. From this kitchen, food and supplies can be delivered to two auxiliary kitchens and twelve pantries on the various decks by means of fourteen dumb-waiters. The crew's dining room is on this deck. The six motorized lifeboats previously referred to are carried on the stern of these decks, three on each deck.

No airplane or airship has yet offered to passengers comfort equal to that provided by steamship or even railway travel.[88] To-morrow's air liner will offer facilities and comforts that are in every respect identical with those offered by the most advanced ocean liner. Passengers aboard this air liner are able to move about as freely as on an ocean liner, enjoying recreations and diversions similar to those to which sea-going passengers are now accustomed. The extent to which this is true appears, I think, if I indicate some of the main features that will be found on the other decks.

The main lounge is forward on Deck 5.[89] Structurally, it is combined with the main wing and is located between the two pontoons. It is one hundred and seventy feet long, sixty-five feet wide, and thirty-six feet or three stories high. In conjunction with other public rooms, such as the library and writing rooms, it accommodates, without crowding, more than the normal number of passengers aboard the plane.

The main dining room, with a seating capacity of two hundred and four persons, is situated to the rear of the lounge. From the main floor of the dining room a double staircase leads to the mezzanine level, where there are additional tables. Inset in one wall of the dining room is an orchestra platform. Three private dining rooms with a capacity of forty people are adjacent to the main dining room and pantries. For

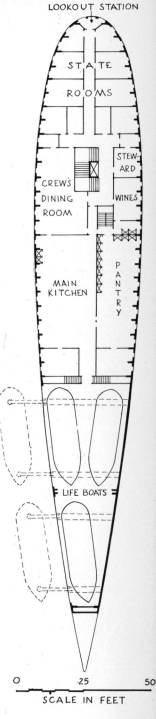

LOOKOUT STATION

STATE ROOMS

STEW-ARD

CREW'S DINING ROOM

WINES

MAIN KITCHEN

PANTRY

LIFE BOATS

0   25   50
SCALE IN FEET

94 · AIR LINER NUMBER 4: DECK 4L
DESIGNED BY NORMAN BEL GEDDES 1929
AERONAUTICAL ENGINEER OTTO KOLLER

recreational purposes in the late evening, the dining room is designed to be transformed into a night club, seating three hundred persons and providing a dance floor for one hundred couples.

On either side of the dining room and connecting the main lounge are two large foyers. From these foyers a wide corridor leads to the sport and recreation decks, with an area of four thousand square feet, providing space for four deck tennis courts, six shuffle-board courts, six quoits, and other games.[95] These decks are entirely enclosed in glass. The gymnasium, which is also on this level, is twenty by twenty-five feet, and is provided with showers and private dressing rooms. Adjacent to the gymnasium is a solarium for men and another for women, each equipped with sixteen couches and with the necessary conveniences, including masseur and masseuse. On this deck are also the children's playroom, the doctor's waiting and consulting room and nurses' quarters, as well as the barber's and the hairdresser's shops. The main bar on this deck has a counter forty feet long and tables in addition. Here, too, is a shop for the sale of miscellaneous articles such as passengers might wish to purchase in the course of a short voyage.

Deck 6 provides the mezzanine levels of the main lounge and dining room, a library, a writing room, and another private dining room for fourteen persons. The main promenade deck (Deck 7) is four hundred and fifty feet long and seventeen feet wide.[96] Running nearly the full length of the main wing on the forward side, with large windows of shatterproof glass along its entire length, passengers are provided

[118]

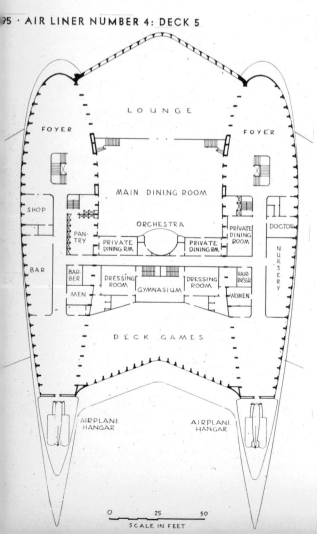

FOYER

LOUNGE

FOYER

SHOP

MAIN DINING ROOM

PAN-TRY

PRIVATE DINING RM.

ORCHESTRA

PRIVATE DINING RM.

PRIVATE DINING ROOM

DOCTOR

BAR

BAR-BER

DRESSING ROOM

GYMNASIUM

DRESSING ROOM

HAIR-DRESSR

NURSERY

MEN

WOMEN

DECK GAMES

AIRPLANE HANGAR

AIRPLANE HANGAR

0   25   50

SCALE IN FEET

DESIGNED BY NORMAN BEL GEDDES 1929
AERONAUTICAL ENGINEER OTTO KOLLER

with the same view and conditions as on the finest ocean liner. Besides providing ample space for passengers to stroll, it accommodates at the same time one hundred and fifty deck chairs. On this deck there is a veranda café with tables for ninety persons.⁹⁶ The main bar adjacent to the café accommodates forty standing at the bar and thirty seated at tables. This bar is equipped with a buffet kitchen and two pantries that connect directly with the main kitchen for convenience in procuring special dishes. On this deck are fourteen suites, consisting of living room, bedroom, and veranda.⁹⁶ Four of these suites have a living room, two bedrooms, and veranda. All have baths and closets. Most are provided with small foyers. All verandas are enclosed with shatterproof glass walls and ceilings. All floors, walls, and ceilings are made of sound-absorbent acoustic board.

On Deck 8, which protrudes forward, are the navigation bridge, chart room and the officers' quarters. The Captain's suite consists of a large draw-

96 · AIR LINEP NUMBER 4: DECK 7
     DESIGNED BY NORMAN BEL GEDDES 1929
     AERONAUTICAL ENGINEER OTTO KOLLER

DECK

VERANDA CAFE

BAR

BATHS

STEWARD   STEWARD

SUITES

VERANDAS

PROMENADE

BATHS

SUITES

VERANDAS

SUITES

AILERON

0   25   50
SCALE IN FEET

ing-room, bedroom and bath. Adjacent to the bridge is the radio receiving and sending station. The office for the station is a separate room which connects with the public hallway. Officers' quarters and passenger staterooms occupy the remainder of this deck.

As previously described, the interior of the auxiliary wing, which houses the engine room, machine and repair shop and motors constitutes Deck 9.[97] Two elevators and two staircases for the use of passengers join Deck 2 to Deck 8.[91] In addition, there are two service staircases for the crew joining all nine decks. A telephone system throughout the ship connects every room. There are, of course, electric light and running water in all rooms.

There are eighteen single staterooms, eighty-one double staterooms, of which twenty-four have private baths, ten suites of three rooms each, ten suites of four rooms each, four suites of six rooms each. The suites have sleeping accommodations for from four to six persons. One hundred and nineteen sleeping rooms have outside windows. Sixty rooms are inside without windows, but are equally well ventilated. The entire ship is hermetically closed at all times and is air conditioned.

Each deck has two or more steward's pantries, with direct dumb-waiter facilities from the main or auxiliary kitchens and with linen and other supply closets adjacent. The crew personnel, numbering one hundred and fifty-five, is sufficiently large to provide excellent service in every department. It consists of the following:

1 Captain	1 Chief Engineer	2 Electricians	1 Baggage Master
1 Mate	2 Engineers	4 Seamen	2 Baggage Men
2 Navigators	7 Mechanics	1 Purser	1 Chief Steward
2 Pilots	2 Radio Operators	1 Cashier	1 Chief Dining-
		2 Telephone	Room Steward
		Operators	2 Head Waiters
		2 Clerks	2 Wine Stewards
		1 Stenographer	24 Waiters
		1 Librarian	7 Bus Boys

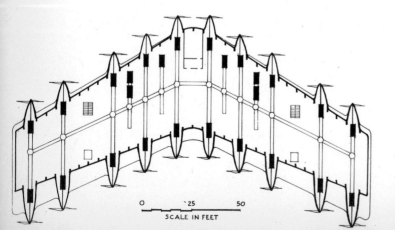

0   25   50
SCALE IN FEET

97 · AIR LINER NUMBER 4: DECK 9
DESIGNED BY NORMAN BEL GEDDES 1929
AERONAUTICAL ENGINEER OTTO KOLLER

1 Chief Bar Steward	6 Cooks	1 Nurse	1 Manicurist
9 Bar Stewards	2 Dishwashers	1 Gymnast	1 Children's Room
1 Chief Deck	24 Room Stewards	1 Masseur	Stewardess
Steward	16 Room Steward-	1 Masseuse	7 Musicians
6 Deck Stewards	esses	1 Barber	1 Shop Attendant
1 Chef	1 Doctor	1 Hairdresser	

This plane has been designed upon the basis of the latest developments in aviation known to-day. Every detail and every principle involved has been tested in one form or another. It is merely the combination that is new.

As to whether, exactly, this type of air liner is the next step in solving the problem of intercontinental aviation is beyond calculation. What can be reasonably anticipated is that a liner its equal in size, facilities, and comfort *will* be a common means of intercontinental transit in the not very remote future. Whether the development of such liners will follow the identical trend I have indicated is problematical. I am inclined to believe that the principles I have followed will be utilized for a few years and that engineers will then have at their command new principles which will make possible further advances and simplifications.

Air liners of a size that is not easily visualized to-day will eventually supplant ocean liners in intercontinental transportation of express traffic-passengers and mail, but not freight. No such radical departure from a long-established mode of transportation can occur without bringing enormous consequences in its train. In many respects, getting the world on wheels has changed the face of the earth. With the prospect of air liners spanning the oceans on scheduled flights, one need not peer very far beyond the horizon to detect other changes that are stimulating to contemplate. Intercontinental aviation will change the whole structure of present-day world metropolises. This is not at all an exaggerated view. Chicago, for instance, under influences that will arise concomitantly with intercontinental aviation, may easily become as much of a world metropolis as New York.

CHAPTER 6

New Houses for Old

Only recently have architects attempted to solve the problems of domestic architecture in terms of the present age. Our best architects of the last generation were trained primarily on the basis of the monumental problem, the big building. The study they have given to dwellings has been from the viewpoint of the expensive home, the mansion, the estate. They have dealt with the house problem as miniature buildings patterned after big ones. Hence, houses have become miniature state capitols in the Georgian style. When they ignored the classical periods, they achieved such results as are typified by the Victorian-Eastlake style."

Owing to the fact that many American architects have been educated abroad, especially in France, we have had the influence of the château and other European styles. Tucked away in their original settings, the charm of these houses is undeniable. So, back they have come to the United States. The more closely the architect kept to the proportions and characteristics of the originals, the better job he believed he had done. But the world has progressed since the day when the originals of these houses were built. They were abreast of the civilization up to their time in terms of domestic conveniences. Masonry was then the material offering the greatest possibilities. But masonry has limitations which are eliminated by to-day's methods based upon the steel frame. In the masonry house, the lower walls have to be heavy and strong enough to support the upper walls, the floors, the roof and everything else, including the live load.[100] To-day, a comparatively light steel framework can do this, so that the walls become part of the weight that the framework carries.

Houses have actually changed very little since the Elizabethan period. Methods of construction and materials used have remained primarily the same. Modern conveniences, such as plumbing, electricity and central heating, have been added. Increased building costs have resulted in skimping on materials and workmanship. Mechanical knickknacks and decorative whatnots have been introduced to hide the deterioration of essential parts.

The outstanding limitations of houses to-day may briefly be summarized as follows: Costs are excessive, due to waste space in planning. Useless rooms such as attic and large cellar add to the expense of construction and upkeep. Little-used rooms such as the dining room and sleeping porches are uneconomical.[101] There is frequently the additional expense of exterior and interior ornament of old styles, Colonial, Tudor, Norman or Spanish, applied over modern construction. Houses are too often planned from the exterior. Rooms are fitted into a Cotswold cottage or a French château, with cramming and inconvenience in consequence. Porches cut off light from adjacent rooms. Heating and ventilation facilities are not thorough. Valuable garden space is given over to the unsightly garage.

As is the case with any other problem of design, the starting point for the house is the organism of its various purposes, the plan. A house is where we spend the greater part of our time. Here we must rest, eat, play. In order to rest, we must sleep. In order to sleep, we should have the most comfortable beds possible and all the fresh air we can get. In the daytime that same sleeping room must be thoroughly aired and sunned. In terms of to-day the most antiquated sleeping room is one with only two average-size windows. As far as health is concerned, the sleeping porch completely open on two or three sides is the ideal. Every sleeping room should be a sleeping porch and a comfortable room at the same time.

98 · JOHN WARD HOUSE, SALEM   DESIGNER UNKNOWN 1684

To eat we must have a place to cook, and the facilities for cooking must be thoroughly organized so as to minimize the amount of foot work on the part of the worker. There are many phases to the cooking job, from ordering to receiving the materials and storing them in an organized and quickly accessible way; having the many utensils instantly available for use; serving the food in the most appetizing manner at its correct temperature; cleaning the dishes, pots and pans after the meal. All of this is an involved problem and until quite recently has been handled in a hit-or-miss fashion. A kitchen should be as well organized as the most efficient factory. It should work with the ease of a machine. As much of the work as possible should, of course, be done by machines.

For play, no matter what form it takes, no matter how small the house, there must be space. Spaciousness is not a matter of size but of proportion. One large room in terms of play is equal to two small ones. A court or a yard that is open and unbroken is worth more than two the same size, if these are broken up. Play takes many forms, indoors and outdoors. Rooms in the house intended for this purpose should be designed to give the utmost flexibility and variety. The drawing-room of two generations ago or the sitting room of the last generation fail when called upon to serve this purpose.

A successful commercial building for various forms of play and amusement is designed from the viewpoint of unbroken space. A house should be designed with similar principles in mind, though on a greatly reduced scale. The living room should be what the term implies. It should not only be thoroughly satisfac-

Brown Brothers

99 · SUBURBAN HOUSE   DESIGNER UNKNOWN 1888

tory for after-dinner conversation; it should be possible easily and instantly to transform it for any kind of party or gathering. It should be easily cleared for dancing. It should be easily thrown open on a delightful summer afternoon in such a manner that it is doubled in size by the terrace outside.

To fulfill its social requirements, a house should have ample space for six times the number of people it is intended to house normally. Furthermore,

[125]

DESIGNED BY WALKER & CARSWELL 1922

there should be nooks and corners where two or more persons can be by themselves, for reading and talking quietly, regardless of anything else that is going on in the house. The children must have their quarters separate from the older people. It is as bad for children to have to be in the continual presence of older people as it is for the older people always to have them around.

A library is essential. Though it may be no larger than a bathroom, it should be a room by itself. Every member of the household should have a place where he can be by himself when he desires, and this place should be inviting. One trouble with the improperly organized house is that there is not enough opportunity for people to see less of each other. They are thrown together constantly, which results in an incentive to get out of the house.

In all its essentials, a house should be as organized as a factory is. For it *is* a factory of a kind; and it is the most difficult kind of factory to run because the business of living has to continue, regardless of world upheavals and general conditions, regardless of personal troubles and complications.

Persons of taste are frequently disposed to object to the so-called new style of things, and particularly when this new style is applied to the house. If they would bear one thought in mind, they would be helped immeasurably. We become accustomed to changes that are real improvements after living with them for a very short time. Habit is a tremendous factor in our lives. A workman would rather continue using an old and awkward tool than accustom himself to a new one, and this is merely because he is accustomed to the old. Once he has become accustomed to the new, however, he would not return to the old. When we look at photographs of examples of these new houses, we say that they do not look homey, or livable, but like operating rooms. This is due merely to the directness with which the purpose is expressed in the design.

Had we been in houses of this kind for any length of time, had we known people who lived in them, had we dined, slept, loafed in them, we would feel differently. In addition, we would find that they are at least twice as easy to take care of as any house we had ever been in. In terms of honest comfort, they have all the advantages, because the whole purpose back of the change

101 · SUBURBAN HOUSE: PLANS   DESIGNED BY WALKER & CARSWELL 1922

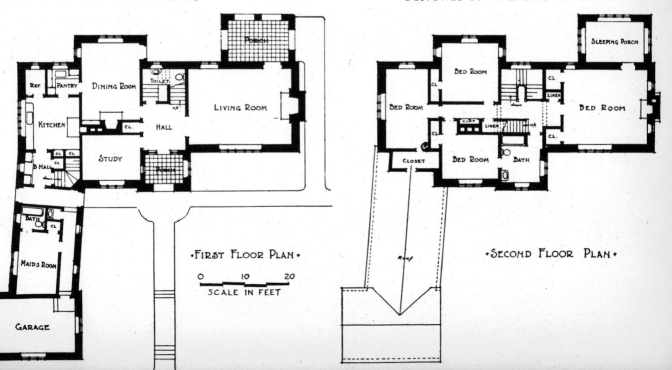

in style is not a thing of appearance but a thing of use. Many people forget that the great majority of examples of contemporary design are extremely poor. They have not been around long enough yet to be discarded, as is the case with many of the older examples of bad design. Time is a great discriminator and time has not yet eliminated the poor examples of contemporary work.

The aim of the house should be to reduce to a minimum the burdensome features of living and to enable the family to have an economical and relaxing home life. The ultimate criterion of the house is the ratio of expense to living value, not a show of superficial decoration. When the job of planning a house according to its purposes and uses is complete, then the individual characteristics of the people living in the house can express themselves and there is no reason to assume that this expression cannot be as complete in a house so organized as in one that is put up helter-skelter.

The ground plot is the starting point for the designing of any house.[102] It should emphasize privacy, time saving, light and sunshine. Scientific planning of the house location requires that the garden and playground should be treated as functions of the house; that every room in the house should be exposed to direct sunlight; that a maximum of green vegetation should be provided. These principles can and should be utilized, not only in connection with the individual house, but in group building plans. Park spaces should be given primary importance; factory and residential sections should be divided by parks, while they remain accessible to each other by modern means of transportation. Community plans may involve the creation of superblocks, containing a series of dead-end streets. These streets should be immune to through traffic, connected internally by a continuous park, and belted around with traffic avenues. To return to the private house — it should be as private as possible. To begin with, in its ground plot if the house is situated near the street, the private "back yard" increases in usability.[102]

The well-planned house requires a group arrangement of the rooms. Passages of communication should be short and time-saving. Living, sleeping, and housekeeping parts of the house should be clearly separated, giving privacy to each group. Proper location of the house on its ground plot gives morning sun to bedrooms, south or western exposures to living rooms and kitchens, while staircases and bathrooms face north.

In house Number 3, the living quarters are at the rear, overlooking the garden.[103] The dining room is an alcove off the living room and separated from it by a change in floor level.[105] The study or library is a separate room, not directly accessible to any other room and consequently additionally private. Sleeping quarters are on the second floor.[106] The owner's bedroom has two dressing rooms, bath and sun terrace overlooking the garden. It is separated from other rooms by a small hall.

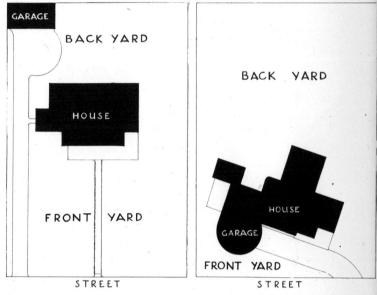

102 · COMPARATIVE PLAN OF HOUSE POSITION ON PLOT

The child's room, terrace and bath are a complete unit and capable of complete isolation in case of contagious diseases.[106] Guest room, bath and small terraces are on the ground floor in a separate wing, so that the guest will not interfere with or be disturbed by the regular household routine.[105] A two-car garage with turntable eliminates the space of a turning place in the drive.[103] The passageway between garage and stairway is a roofed and walled part of the whole structure.

Kitchen, pantry, maid's room and bath, and the service entrance, are organized as one unit.[105] The pantry opens directly into the dining alcove, and it is of sufficient width to permit the dining-room table to be rolled into the pantry, where dishes are set and removed before and after meals. The maid's room is directly under the child's room, so that she can hear the cries of the child when the family is away. A combined sewing room and linen closet is on the second floor.[106] Here, built-in cupboards are fitted for towels, sheets and other supplies. Cedar-lined storage space, sewing machine, ironing board, and cutting counter are all provided for. Communicating passages are short and compact and arranged to give a maximum amount of privacy to each room of the house. The entrance hall is small and connects directly with the stair hall, living, and servants' quarters, though none are visible from it.[105] The stair hall, the center of family activity, is not visible from any room in the house.

In the elements of its structure, the modern house may differ, considerably, if not radically, from the wall-bearing structure to which we have been accustomed. If it has a steel frame, the interior and exterior walls, partitions, floors and roof are all carried by this skeleton structure. Skeleton construction has two major economies to recommend it. The frame itself can be made of relatively few shapes that require little handling and small space. In addition, the old-fashioned heavy bearing wall is replaced by thin, stiff,

103 · HOUSE NUMBER 3   DESIGNED BY NORMAN BEL GEDDES 1930

Maurice Goldberg

104 · HOUSE NUMBER 3   DESIGNED BY NORMAN BEL GEDDES 1930

lightweight and inexpensive curtain walls that are more easily assembled. In a house so constructed, the partitions have no structural relation to floor or façade; they serve only to limit various usable spaces. Partitions on the second floor need not be over those on the first floor. These partitions should be thin membranes of sufficient stiffness and acoustical insulation, light in weight and with an appropriate surface.

The structural function of a bearing wall is of paramount importance, inasmuch as the walls support not only their own weight but the floor and roof loads as well.[101] They must be thick, strong, and may be pierced for windows or doors only when additional provision is made to support the loads over such openings. A curtain wall system is characterized by a structural frame which carries all floor and wall loads directly to the foundation. It is enclosed in a relatively thin envelope of masonry metal, glass or other material suitable for keeping out the weather, heat or cold, through which openings may be pierced at random. In house Number 3 the curtain walls are either of precast or poured concrete.

With curtain wall construction, the window area can be greatly increased. Windows may extend from floor to ceiling and from partition to parti-

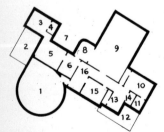

KEY PLAN TO FIRST FLOOR

1. Garage
2. Service Porch
3. Maid's Room
4. Bath
5. Kitchen
6. Pantry
7. Terrace
8. Dining Alcove
9. Living Room
10. Guest Room
11. Bath
12. Entrance Porch
13. Entrance Hall
14. Lavatory
15. Library
16. Stair Hall

DESIGNED BY NORMAN BEL GEDDES 1930

KEY PLAN TO SECOND FLOOR

17. Children's Terrace
18. Children's Room
19. Closet
20. Bath
21. Stair Hall
22. Sewing Room
23. Bedroom
24. Bath

25. Hall
26. Master Bedroom
27. Wife's Dressing
     Room
28. Husband's Dressing
     Room
29. Bath
30. Master's Terrace

tion.[107] Isolated windows give a harsh light and opaque walls between windows prevent an increase of light where needed. Bands or continuous window sheets reflect a diffused light to the farthest corner of a room;[108] shades and curtains are used to control the intensity of light in the same manner as the lens of a camera. In this house, the windows are sealed; they are used solely to admit light and the beneficial sun rays.

With modern construction methods, the pitched roof[100] becomes unnecessary.[104] An insulating medium can take the place of the space-wasting attic with its wooden frames and trusses. The steel framework is easily able to support the weight of accumulated snow. Flat roofs can be utilized as terraces, increasing the livable area of the house.[105] The roof terraces of house Number 3 are an integral part of the plan. The child's terrace is over the garage.[106] Its high parapet, concrete umbrella, and sand box make it an ideal and safe playground in summer and winter. The terrace off the owner's bedroom,[106] with its vine-covered trellis, can be used for sun baths and as a private retreat.

The design of house Number 3 specifies that all wiring shall be placed inside non-corrosive conduits in the floors, walls, and between the steel channels of the metal lath partitions and accessible throughout. Built-in, indirect lighting is used throughout. Correct lighting of a room demands a general diffused light for illuminating the entire room and a localized light in particular places for such activities as working, reading and eating. Despite their simplicity, the old-fashioned methods of lighting a room, regardless of their picturesqueness, were never successful. The chandelier so commonly used provided a disconcerting illumination that necessitated shades being attached to it so that the glare might be softened. This measure defeated its own purpose, for the result was a number of spotlights which poured their illumination straight down and thereby failed to light up the room as a whole.

107 · HOUSE NUMBER 3: LIVING ROOM   DESIGNED BY NORMAN BEL GEDDES 1930

For example, place the sources of light in the cornice structure, where walls and ceiling meet, and the result is an indirect diffused light of ample strength. Or set banks of bulbs into the ceiling itself, with reflectors backing them and translucent plates covering the recess. Properly designed, this arrangement is both a source of light by night and a simple ceiling scheme by day. Translucent plates set in the ceiling can emphasize the shape and proportions of a room. The plates give added interest in the daytime, if they are edged with black vitrolite, especially when this edging contrasts with a pale gray ceiling and pearly white glass.

I carried over an idea from the theater that has met with approval in the architectural field. A light intensity control, built into the wiring circuit, permits the use of any intensity of light that may be desired under varying conditions. By merely pressing a button, the light can be brightened or softened imperceptibly, or hold any particular intensity as long as desired. This variable-intensity feature is a decided addition to lighting comfort and may be made fully automatic by the use of the photoëlectric cell. This type of lighting was first installed in the Conference Hall of the J. Walter Thompson Company offices.[191]

In house Number 3, radiators, hidden in the walls, are placed directly under the windows, extending their full width, insuring a more even distribution of warm air. Artificial or forced ventilation, with hermetically sealed windows, eliminates dust and germs. The outside air is filtered, humidified or dried, heated or cooled, to keep the house at the desired temperature and humidity.

DESIGNED BY NORMAN BEL GEDDES 1930

Better workmanship and lower costs for the modern house will presently be achieved through factory fabrication of standardized story heights, beam spans, walls, partitions, floor sections and equipment units. Mass fabrication of sections will permit rapid assembly and ease of finishing, thus reducing cost of labor. The importance of this in to-morrow's life is beyond comprehension at the moment but can readily be appreciated in view of the fact that the cost of labor for finishing alone is usually estimated as twelve per cent of the construction cost. Eventually, it will be possible to purchase from the factory mechanized rooms, such as bathroom and unit kitchen, already set up. My own staff has been working for some time on kitchen units so standardized that the sink, stove and cabinet are component parts of a single standardized unit. Such unit kitchens will have the advantage of simplicity and attractiveness as well as economy in cost and better organization.

The kitchen of the modern house demands well-planned lighting in addition to step-saving arrangements and labor-saving, mechanical devices. An oblong kitchen, when designed to order, should have windows on both long sides to afford plenty of light.[105] The color scheme used in a kitchen can enhance or hinder its serviceability. Neutral tones are not only restful to the eyes but also reflect light most effectively. Because such tones are used, the kitchen and pantry need not be dull and uninteresting.[109]

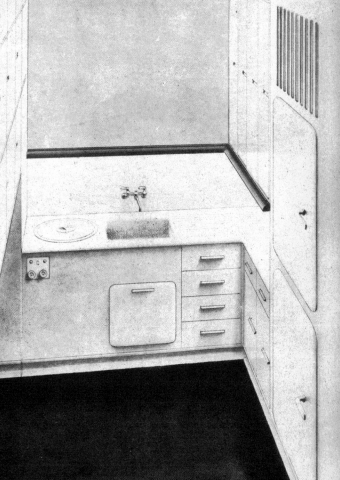

109 · HOUSE NUMBER 3: PANTRY
DESIGNED BY NORMAN BEL GEDDES 1930

Cheerfulness is easily obtained by cheerfully colored curtains and equipment. Walls with a dull finish are preferable because they do not cause glare. Material used should of course be impervious to moisture, with a hard surface that can be easily cleaned, such as metal, matt tile, or hard plaster finished with oil paint or lacquer. The floor for the kitchen and pantry should be chosen with particular care because no other floor surface has to stand half so much wear. Floors of cork or rubber composition not only wear remarkably well but are easily washed.

Built-in furniture and other built-in equipment give the house added spaciousness. Built-in bathroom, kitchen, nursery equipment, cupboards, cabinets, bookshelves, desks and sofas should be an integral part of the original plan of the modern home. The library of house Number 3 exemplifies the advantages of built-in furniture.[108] Built-in bookshelves occupy two walls from floor to ceiling. A built-in desk under the window in one corner and running along another wall gives space for typewriter, drawers for paper, table area for writing, and magazines. Built-in furniture strikingly reveals some of the beneficial results of properly coördinating the architecture and decoration of a house. For convenience, some pieces of furniture should be movable, but cupboards, sofas, and similar unwieldly pieces are readily fixed in places individually designed for them. One advantage gained is their unity with the other fixed features of the house and the elimination of dust-catching spaces behind and under them.

The beauty of the modern dwelling house is the logical result of emphasis upon its functional values. Open walls let in an abundance of sunshine and light which are both physical and spiritual assets. The successful structure typifies the buoyancy of life. Its clearly defined, simple forms are devoid of imitation and false show, and there is a harmony of proportion between all the parts. This is in keeping with the aim of the modern house — to assure complete satisfaction of every material and psychic need of the owner.

Architectural design is becoming more and more an expression of integrity. This is exemplified by built-in furniture. Not long ago the architect did not consider furnishings as an integral part of his design. He left the furnishings to the client or a " decorator " and the result in the majority of cases looked like it. Interior decoration in its general expression is applied rather than organic – a matter of whims rather than necessity.

CHAPTER 7

Industrializing the Theater

CASUAL observers of the course of events in the theater will say that the theater is not an industrial activity. Many of those who work in the theater will be still more emphatic about it. This is one of the major troubles with our theater, and this lack in our theater is a lack in our life. Drama goes hand in hand with the progress and achievements of humanity. The theater to-day needs the same aggressive spirit of experimentation that characterizes progressive industry. The quality of our drama would be enhanced if the theater were industrialized, which implies a modern and economical organization, financial structure and stabilization.

The greatest progress that has recently taken place in the theater is within the confines of Russia. If there is any place where the theater is approaching a successful industrialization it is in Russia at the present moment. There, all theatrical entertainment is controlled and operated by the Government after the manner of a single industrial activity. They have gone at the theater with the same spirit and energy that they have gone at the building of tractors and dams, only they have been more successful because their dramatic talent is in excess of their engineering talent. The theater in Russia is considered a fundamental necessity in terms of public education and recreation.

In the United States, there is nothing comparable to the organized theater as it exists in Russia, Germany or France. By an organized theater I do not mean a real-estate concern, nor merely a well-organized business office engaging and operating its talent on a tentative basis. The nearest approach we have now to an industrialized theater is the organization maintained by the Theater Guild of New York. The annual costs of this organization are assured by their subscribers. They are thus encouraged to produce a play that they believe to be good, even though they are not sure that it will run more than the six weeks required to enable all their subscribers to see it. If it does, they make a profit. It it doesn't, they lose nothing.

The subscribers, on the other hand, are enabled to see the plays at a considerably reduced rate by subscribing to all six of the Theater Guild's annual productions in advance. True, all of the subscribers may not care for one or two of the plays that are done each season, but they might feel the same way about plays produced by other managements. Payment in advance with the risk of witnessing a play that may not develop into a popular success is offset by the fact that any successful play produced by another management would probably cost two or three times the subscription price for a Guild success. Thus, in the long run, the Guild subscribers more than break even, financially and intellectually.

Although the building to house such an organization as I have in mind is decidedly a secondary factor in its ultimate success, nevertheless it is that phase of the subject to which we are limited here. A factory, an office, a man's desk, or his wife's house functions in accordance with the way it is organized. Satisfactory operation depends upon thoroughness in terms of performance. The most efficient kitchen is the one in which the greatest number of frequently used articles are available in the shortest space of time, with the least number of steps on the part of the person doing the work. The same principle applies generally, and it applies to the theater.

I doubt if there are any factories where employees are more on their feet and have to waste more steps than actors do in the theater. The unnecessary distances they have to travel are frequently enormous, owing, for instance, to the location of dressing rooms in relation to the stage. Not only actors but executives and lesser members of the personnel are handicapped by numberless similar disadvantages. The theater not only possesses many of the complications of a factory but also of a school and educational system. It is due to the fact that it is made up of all these elements and more, that it should be industrialized.

A theater should be so planned that all of the departmental units, involved in the creation of a theatrical production, should be properly organized in relation to one another and to the whole. These units should include the housing (in a work sense) of executives, the actors, and all other persons necessary to a production; housing requirements for the production of material such as scenery and costumes, and for storage; and, in addition, provision for social and recreational activities, schooling and training facilities.

The first requisite of the theater is that along with everything else it must furnish recreation. If the audience cannot be induced into a state of restfulness, of pleasure, of enjoyment, of receptiveness to entertainment, one cannot do with them what he wills, and this is necessary to achieve results in terms of the theater. The audience must be made susceptible to an exaggerated extent. The spontaneity of youth, combined with sufficient intelligence to react to other than merely obvious points, is within every audience. To give an audience recreation, the theater must at the same time stimulate it.

In many ways, the present-day plan of our theaters does not contribute to this end. The interiors of most theaters to-day are horrible examples[110] of not only bad taste but lack of theatrical foresight. The auditorium of any theater has a definite effect upon the receptivity of an audience, not only during a performance but prior to it. The auditorium, and more especially that part adjacent to the stage, should be as simple and neutral as possible in architectural and decorative treatment. The judgment, taste and design exemplified in ninety-five per cent of the theaters of America is the most atrocious display of bad taste and waste of money that I know of anywhere. The theaters of no country in the world can compare with those of the United States in vulgar and cheap architectural decoration. In all, there are not more than a dozen thoroughly appropriate and good-looking theater interiors in our country.

An auditorium should not be considered as a thing apart from the stage. It should not be looked upon as a big hall with one wall knocked out, so that you seem to look into another room where a story is enacted. It should be of such a character that the moment the scene is disclosed on the stage you

110 · ROXY THEATER, NEW YORK
DESIGNED BY WALTER W. AHLSCHLAGER 1927

Tebbs & Knell

forget that you are in a theater. In this respect, a great deal depends, of course, upon the performance. Nevertheless, the best of performances is at a disadvantage in most of our theaters. The test of a designer or of an architect comes when you ask him to do something simply. Any one can take a vast wall surface and break it up with gingerbread decoration of the gewgaw variety. But tell this same decorator that your taste is of a different order, that he may not do this for you, that you like quiet restful surroundings, that in fact you insist upon it — and see what happens! But be careful of your man — for there is a great difference between a wall surface kept *simple* in the hands of a fine, sensitive designer and one that is only left *bare* by a less able man.

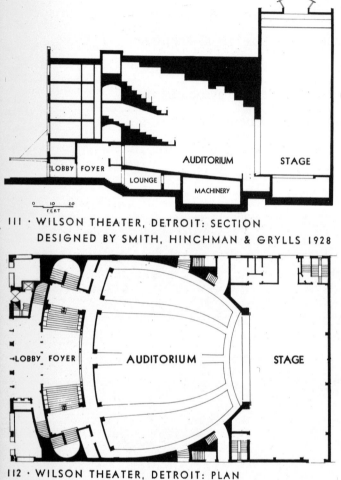

III · WILSON THEATER, DETROIT: SECTION
DESIGNED BY SMITH, HINCHMAN & GRYLLS 1928

112 · WILSON THEATER, DETROIT: PLAN
DESIGNED BY SMITH, HINCHMAN & GRYLLS 1928

The Repertory Theater (a development of Theater Number 6) is one conception of a building to house an industrialized theater[115] on a scale practical for any large city. Since it was designed for the proposed Chicago World Fair, it spreads out over more ground than it would if planned to occupy a portion of a city block. It contains four different types of theaters and every other element necessary for producing, rehearsing and storing productions under one roof.

The central tower of this building is nineteen stories high. It houses rehearsal rooms, workshops, scenery storage space, offices, and over one hundred large dressing rooms, each having outside windows and showers. From this

[144]

tower radiate a cabaret, a roof garden, a theater for children, one large theater, and one intimate theater.[117]

The cabaret and roof garden accommodate two hundred and fifty persons. The main dining room is two stories high, with a balcony around the second floor. Kitchen and pantries are in the basement, with service elevators. Directly across from the entrance is a circular orchestra pit sunk below the level of the dance floor, and from which the dance floor radiates. Behind the orchestra pit is an elevated stage, with steps on either side leading down to the dance floor. A movable screen regulates the depth of the stage. The roof garden is rectangular in plan, with four terraces and a small circular orchestra space. A circular stair and elevator rises from the lobby to the balcony and roof garden.

There is a small theater for children, of the proscenium type, seating two hundred children on the main floor and sixty adults in a balcony where they would be almost invisible to the children.[117] The stage is equipped so that it can also be used for marionette shows. This theater is rectangular in shape, with two side aisles. Above the auditorium is a rehearsal room. On the roof are terraces for outdoor dances, gymnasium exercises, and rehearsals.

The adult large and small auditoriums are identical in plan.[117] The large auditorium seats seventeen hundred and the small auditorium seven hundred and fifty people. In both, the main axis of stage and auditorium is on the diagonal of the square.

If ten architects were employed to design ten theaters to meet the specifications of

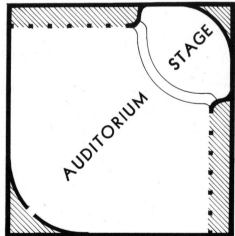

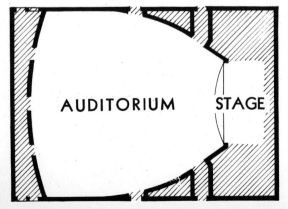

ten "practical" theatrical business men, these ten theaters, as regards stage and auditorium, would almost certainly duplicate one another in all fundamental features. In each, we would have the conventional rectangular stage against one side of the rectangle, footlights along the front of the stage, visible orchestra pit, and the proscenium arch framing the stage and definitely separating audience from actors.[111-112]

If a designer conversant by long experience with the limitations of the present theater were given the same opportunity, he would undoubtedly design stage and auditorium without regard for the conventional peep-show pattern, considering not tradition but the needs of to-day's dramatists, directors, and actors. There are many ways of solving the problem. In 1914 I evolved one solution which has several advantages and has been utilized in over fifty theaters by various architects since its description by Claude Bragdon in The Architectural Record of September, 1922. Given two ground plots identical in square foot area: on the one hand, the typical theater with the auditorium and stage centered on the *longitudinal* axis of the plot.[113] On the other hand, a theater with the auditorium and stage centered on the *diagonal* axis.[114] The shaded areas of each diagram represent the space not utilized by the audience while sitting in their seats, witnessing the play. The efficient, unshaded area in the longitudinal axis theater at the left is fifty-six per cent. The efficient area in the diagonal axis principle is eighty-four per cent. Furthermore, the total depth of the stage in the left plan is only twenty-five feet, while the stage depth of the diagonal axis theater is forty feet. The stage area in the diagonal axis theater is twice that of the other. So much for the basic features. The diagonal axis principle has been applied in both of the theaters in the Repertory Theater group.[117]

Imagine yourself entering an auditorium without aisles. The stage is not framed by an arch and is without a curtain — apparently as open as outdoors.

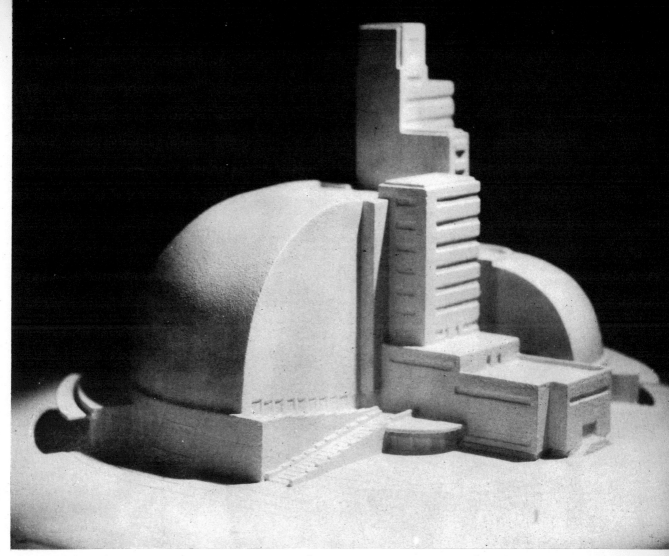

115 · REPERTORY THEATER

In fact, due to its illumination, you can see nothing on it — it is a spacious void. Not even an orchestra pit is to be seen. The curved front of the stage is separated from the spectators merely by a low line of steps along its entire width. From an orchestra pit that is not in view, but is nevertheless between audience and actors and from which the conductor may see all of the auditorium and stage without being seen, come strains of music. Arranged in quarter circles concentric with the curve of the stage front, widely separated rows of seats form an amphitheater without being interrupted by aisles. Each

[147]

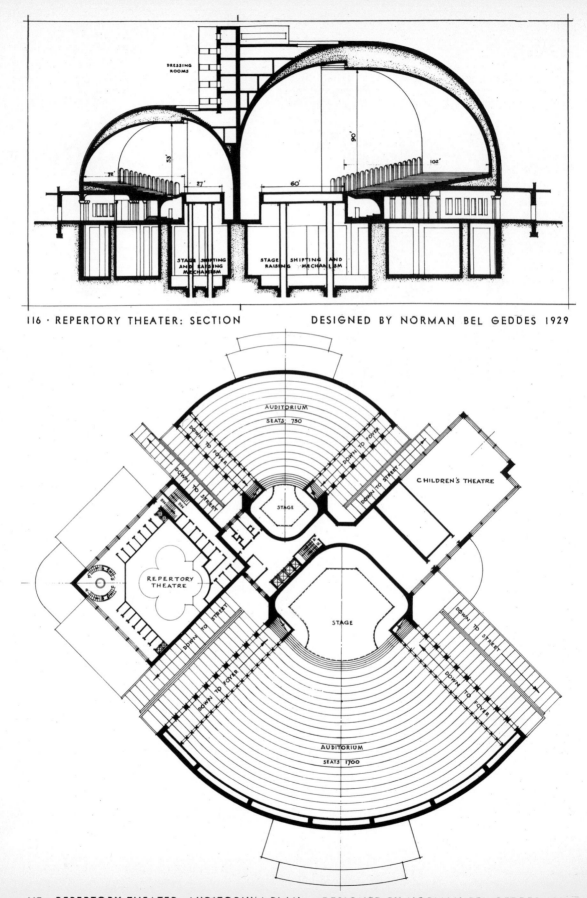

116 · REPERTORY THEATER: SECTION   DESIGNED BY NORMAN BEL GEDDES 1929

117 · REPERTORY THEATER: AUDITORIUM PLAN   DESIGNED BY NORMAN BEL GEDDES 1929

row of seats is its own aisle. You reach your seat by passing along an aisle-wide space that separates your row from the row in front, without stumbling over the feet of any one already seated.

Except for the low flight of steps at the front of the stage and two softly curving side jams which lose themselves in the curve of the ceiling, the stage

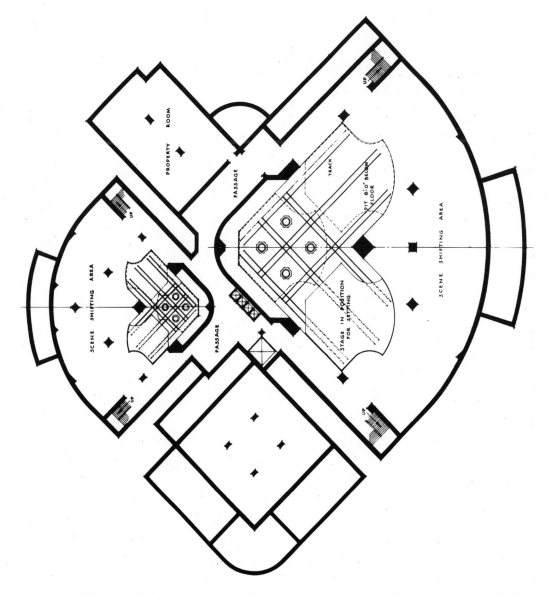

118 · REPERTORY THEATER: BASEMENT PLAN   DESIGNED BY NORMAN BEL GEDDES 1929

is undivided from the auditorium."⁵ Thus, a sense of unity, intimacy, and audience-participation pervades the theater, arising in part from the fact that the same great domed ceiling spans actors and audience."⁶ By the indicated seating arrangement, each person is allowed nearly twice the amount of floor space usually allotted."⁷ The space between any two rows of seats is four and a half feet, the entrances being from either side instead of from the back. Every seat has plenty of leg room. There are no balconies or galleries.

In a theater of this sort, the scene shifter will find the long-accepted appurtenances of his trade conspicuous by their absence. Looking aloft, he sees the vast sweep of the cyclorama constituting both walls and ceiling, and nowhere the customary wilderness of ropes, curtains, battens and borders. The scenery is set on two movable platforms in the basement."⁸ These platforms are raised and lowered by hydraulic power to and from the level of the auditorium. In their elevated position at the auditorium level they form the stage floor. One stage platform is being " set " while the other is being played; the substitution, which takes only thirty seconds, is made behind a curtain of light or a moment's darkness. The stage lowers into a shallow pit which brings its floor level with the basement floor."⁶ Without stopping, it is carried from this position to one side, a distance equal to its diameter, on tracks set in the floor of the pit. The other stage, already " set " for the next scene, automatically slides into position and is raised to the auditorium level.

No curtain is required in this theater. The most elaborate or simple change of scene can be made in less time than is required for a " quick change " by the present method. To comply with the law of most States, a steel curtain is provided for purposes of emergency to separate the basement, where the scenery is, from the auditorium. It is on the ceiling of the basement and slides horizontally across the opening. Since every row of seats has its own direct exit there are twice as many exits as in the ordinary type of theater. As the result of a lecture given by me in 1922 at the invitation of Harvey Corbett at the New York Architectural League, the New York State Standard Building Code was revised in 1924 to permit this type of curtain and stage.

Underneath the auditorium, there is a broad, quadrant-shaped foyer, serving as a spacious promenade, with smoking rooms, café, and other auxiliary spaces adjacent.[116] On this same level, below the steps leading from the auditorium to the stage, is the orchestra chamber.[116] The sound comes through perforations in the risers of the steps. The orchestra room accommodates sixty musicians. The conductor has a clear view of the stage and auditorium by means of a large rotating periscope, situated in the center of the first row of seats.

Light galleries are set into the dome of the auditorium and are controlled from the stage switchboard. The lamps are located above and behind the spectators and concealed from them. The stage switchboard is located as is the orchestra, and the electrician through his periscope has a clear view of stage and auditorium. One of the outstanding distinctions of modern stagecraft, though very little used, is the extraordinary extent to which light can be made to intensify any scene, serious or comic, in any type of production. Changes of

119 · THEATER NUMBER 6: STAGE
DESIGNED BY NORMAN BEL GEDDES 1914

120 · DANTE'S DIVINE COMEDY: STAGE

DESIGNED BY NORMAN BEL GEDDES 1920

scene and of people can be made in darkness with no curtain necessary to cut off the audience from what is happening on the stage. By a skillful use of light, objects can be revealed or concealed at will. Costumes can be transformed. Convincingly distinctive locales can be suggested without scenery — only a property or two — entirely by light manipulation. The theater I propose, with scene and actors thrust forward into the auditorium instead of being kept behind the proscenium picture frame, takes on a still greater value for both actor and audiences and becomes desirable and practicable, due largely to the great advance of the last decade in the use and control of artificial light.

The conventional theater with its proscenium frame is adaptable only to the peep-show type of play, which has adapted itself to the peep-show type of theater. It is a purely two-dimensional medium and seldom used in more than the across-stage dimension. It is not at all suitable for the presentation of such three-dimensional forms of staging as are necessary to obtain correct values from Greek and Elizabethan or Oriental drama, nor for the new, oncoming drama that will develop as a natural consequence of present-day thought and feeling. These restrictions which are now generally taken for

121 · DIVINE COMEDY THEATER   DESIGNED BY NORMAN BEL GEDDES 1929

granted impose very confining limitations on the dramatist, clipping the wings of inspiration and depriving drama of the freedom and the privileges that are accorded the novel and the cinema. The release of dramatist, director, actor, and audience from the limitations of the present-day conventional theater will not of itself bring about great drama. A great deal depends upon the spirit, power and clarity of expression of a human being. Nevertheless, a human being who expresses himself through what we call a creative medium is most susceptible to his environment, the conditions and the limitations around him, especially to those under which he is obliged to work. The release of dramatists, directors, actors and audiences from the limitations of the present-day conventional type of theater would be a tremendous stimulus for the drama. There is no type of presentation that would not decidedly profit by it.

The thing that is to-day holding back this desirable change is the type of manager who is in the theater primarily for the money he can make out of it.

[153]

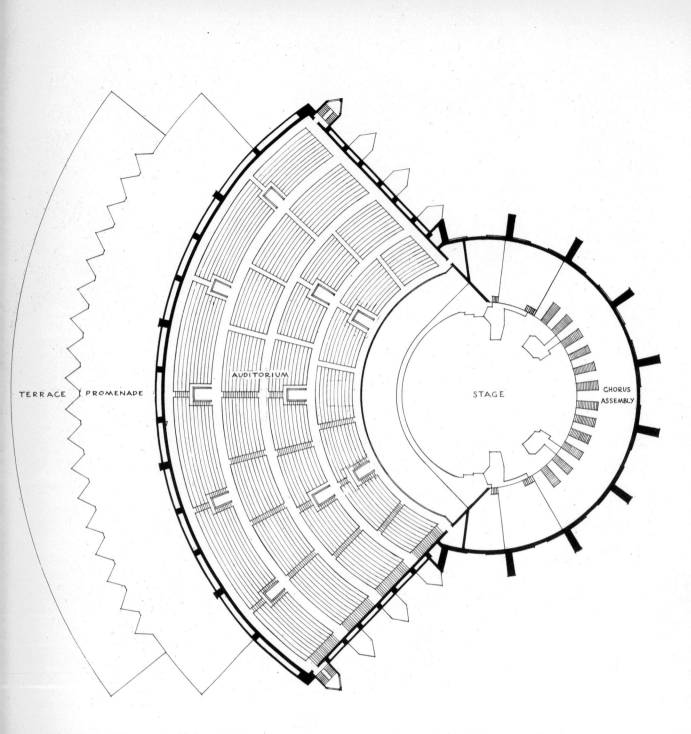

TERRACE | PROMENADE

AUDITORIUM

STAGE

CHORUS
ASSEMBLY

122 · DIVINE COMEDY THEATER: AUDITORIUM PLAN   DESIGNED BY NORMAN BEL GEDDES 1929

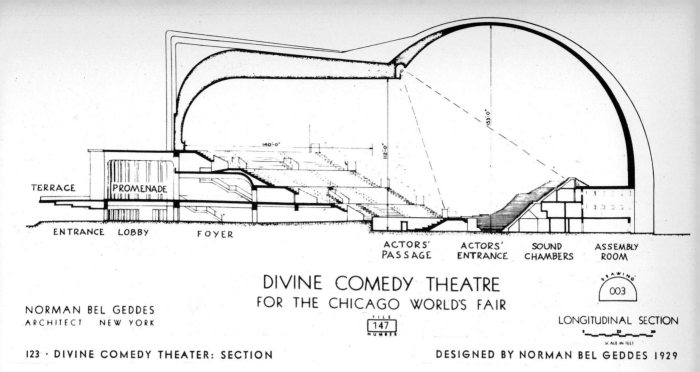

TERRACE PROMENADE

ENTRANCE LOBBY FOYER

ACTORS' ACTORS' SOUND ASSEMBLY
PASSAGE ENTRANCE CHAMBERS ROOM

DIVINE COMEDY THEATRE
FOR THE CHICAGO WORLD'S FAIR

NORMAN BEL GEDDES
ARCHITECT NEW YORK

003

LONGITUDINAL SECTION

123 · DIVINE COMEDY THEATER: SECTION   DESIGNED BY NORMAN BEL GEDDES 1929

For instance, the Shuberts are not in the theatrical producing business at all
in the true sense of the word. They are real-estate operators who produce
plays so that their theaters may not be empty.

From the viewpoint of real-estate operators, who are incidentally theatrical
producers, they reason that there is a distinct advantage in building every
stage like every other one. They mount their productions with the same logic.
They have innumerable storehouses of scenery, costumes and other equipment
from past shows waiting to be used on one of these stages. Not one tenth of
this material is used annually. But what is used is monotonously repeti-
tious. The principle of standardization is right but a principle that does not
produce quality is being used wrongly. With a little ingenuity in design,
a better economical record could be achieved and gain the equally important latitude and variety necessary to a permanently successful theater
organization.

If, instead of seventy theaters in New York, all of identically the same
type, we had seventy of seven different types, it would seem that the problem
would be more complicated. On the contrary! In Russia and Germany that is

exactly the situation and there is nothing in the least complicated about it. The assumption that different types of theaters would complicate the theatrical situation is somewhat like saying that it would complicate matters for a motor-car manufacturer to build a roadster in the same factory in which he builds a limousine. The point is that this desirable change could and should be brought about, and when a thing should be done, there is always a way.

There is no more emphatic way of bringing an idea to the attention of a mass audience and doing it with great force and conviction than in the theater. A play with a strong idea has an amazing effect upon hundreds of thousands of people in a short space of time. The trouble is that so few plays have an idea of any value more than momentary entertainment. Dramatists to-day are in a rut. One follows another in endless repetition. With one or two exceptions annually, those who do experiment turn out half-baked results.

We know that the world has experienced at least one great theater; a theater of momentous power and inspiration, regardless from what standpoint it is considered; a theater that drew audiences five times as large as any motion-picture theater we have to-day. That theater belonged to the Greeks a few hundred years B. C. The object of the Greek theater may be said to have been the rousing of vast, overwhelming tides of thought and feeling in the masses. In modern times we have nothing to compare with this. Between the Greek dramatic phenomena and the theatrical fare with which we are familiar, there is a vast difference.

As a result of thought on this subject, some ten years ago, I designed a stage that would fulfill the necessary dramatic requirements for producing the " Divine Comedy " of Dante.[120] The stage is designed for this production alone, but it could be used for other dramas on a similar scale. Recently, the plans for a theater to house it were completed at the request of the Architectural Commission of the Chicago World's Fair.[121] Architecturally, it provides all the necessary facilities, such as assembly rooms, dressing rooms, foyers, promenade and open-air terrace for the production of a great variety of spectacles and for the accommodation of a mass audience. The auditorium of this theater is designed to accommodate five thousand people.[122] Like a Greek theater, its plan is a half-circle facing the stage without balconies. No proscenium or curtain divides the auditorium from the stage. A great single dome spans the stage and part of the auditorium; the remaining part of the auditorium is covered by a ceiling that joins the dome and curves down into the side walls.[123]

In the United States, we have nothing to compare with Oberammergau, or the Bayreuth Festival or the Salzburg Festival. They were the creation and the spirit of their age. For our age, we have as yet found no equivalent. There are millions of people, most of them from the Old Country, in our industrial communities, who have an inherent liking for such forms of entertainment. Do you realize what it would mean to such communities[124] to have theaters that they could use for *their kind* of entertainment? It is conceivable that industry may eventually recognize the importance of furnishing the organization and financial structure upon which such an effort would depend. Considering the tremendous sums industrial philanthropists have spent for widespread material benefits, and for intellectual beneficiaries such as col-

124 · HOMESTEAD, PENNSYLVANIA

leges and libraries, it is conceivable that they will recognize the value of such an idea to their community.

The Russian Government recognizes the tremendous value of the theater and its fast growing offspring, motion pictures. It has heavily financed several of the largest and most enterprising theatrical and motion-picture companies in the world. Of the Russian theater America knows little for the reason that none of its companies have left Russia. Several of their film productions have been shown in the United States and have had tremendous effect on our own picture technique. Two of them I rank among the half dozen finest pictures that have ever been made. The significant fact is the Russians' recognition of the importance of the theater as a relief for the pent-up emotional capacity of their mass audience. The problem in America takes rank with the ever increasing problem of living not materially but spiritually. It has nothing to do with making a living. The outstanding error that is being made in this age and the most justifiable criticism of the age, is that not enough attention is being given to this other side of life.

CHAPTER 8

Architecture for the Amusement Industry

Some three years ago Doctor Allen D. Albert, on behalf of Rufus Dawes, President of the Chicago World's Fair, requested me to develop a program of theatrical entertainment for the Fair. Their hope was that it would be of a different variety and of a more constructive kind than that usually assembled on exposition grounds. Considerable thought having been given the subject, a plan was embodied in a letter which was submitted to Mr. Dawes and his associates.

Upon the approval of Mr. Dawes, I sent a letter outlining the plan in a general way to a few persons of international standing in the creative phases of the theater, including Granville Barker, Josef Capek, Jean Cocteau, Jacques Copeau, Gordon Craig, Alexandra Exter, Paul Green, Isaac Grunewald, Jean Hugo, Leopold Jessner, Louis Jouvet, Robert Edmond Jones, Georg Kaiser, Visvolod Meyerhold, Eugene O'Neill, Georges Pitoeff, Emil Pirchan, Luigi Pirandello, Isaac Rabinovitch, Max Reinhardt, Oscar Schlemmer, Constantin Stanislavsky, Igor Stravinski, Edward Sturm, Alexander Tairoff, Richard Teschner, Van H. Wijdeveld.

This letter of October 23, 1929, asked for comments on my proposed method of arriving at a plan, suggestions, especially in regard to the organization that should be set up, matters of personnel, types of theaters to be built, types of plays to be produced, dramatists to be commissioned, and so on. The gist of the plan as set forth in my letter may be indicated by the following excerpt:

... The Board of Governors desires to bring together the outstanding theatrical talent of the world, in so far as such a thing is possible, and to select this talent not for what it has done, nor for reputation, but for its potentialities toward various future developments in the theater; with the idea not so much of showing but of *inspiring* varied forms of dramatic expression in writing, staging and acting. The program, briefly, in its present state, is as follows: to erect several theaters distinctly radical and free in their form and proportions, offering unlimited scope to every type but especially to encourage new forms of dramatic writing; to invite the outstanding dramatists of the world either to write plays especially for these theaters or to submit plays to us for premier production — these to be of a distinctly experimental type; to bring to Chicago, sufficiently in advance, six or eight of the younger and more forward-looking directors and designers from various parts of the world, each of whom would stage two different plays under the best conditions. . . .

It had been agreed that the theatrical

125 · THEATER NUMBER 14: AIRPLANE VIEW
DESIGNED BY NORMAN BEL GEDDES 1922

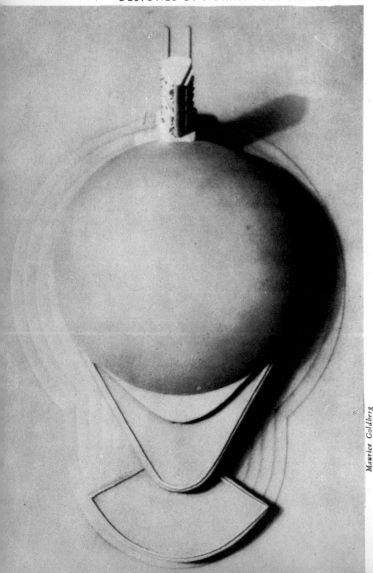

Maurice Goldberg

126 · THEATER NUMBER 14   DESIGNED BY NORMAN BEL GEDDES 1922

fare within the exposition grounds should differ radically from the entertainment offered in the standard Chicago theaters, to eliminate any element of competition.

The letter met with more enthusiasm than I had anticipated. With only two exceptions, constructive replies of ten to twenty pages came in reply. As a result of this program, the Architectural Commission for the Chicago World's Fair associated me with them in the capacity of advisor on theatrical matters, and likewise appointed me to design the exterior illumination of the buildings and grounds. The first direct assignment I was given was to furnish a few concrete examples of various types of theater and restaurant architecture. These structures were to be apart from the general run of theaters and.

restaurants. In the case of the theaters, they were to vary sufficiently in form so as to impose on directors requirements and points of view new to America.

Up to the time of the financial crash, these designs were an integral part of the architectural program. The economic situation has affected the plans for the Fair and only those buildings are being built that are absolutely essential to making the revised program effective. Of the five theaters described below, four were designed for the Fair. They indicate, I believe, and not too

127 · THEATER NUMBER 14: AUDITORIUM PLAN
DESIGNED BY NORMAN BEL GEDDES 1922

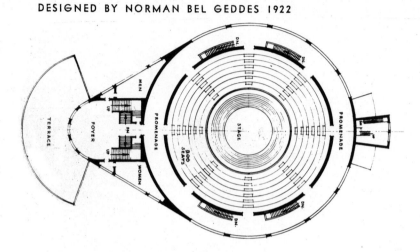

128 · THEATER NUMBER 14: GROUND FLOOR PLAN
DESIGNED BY NORMAN BEL GEDDES 1922

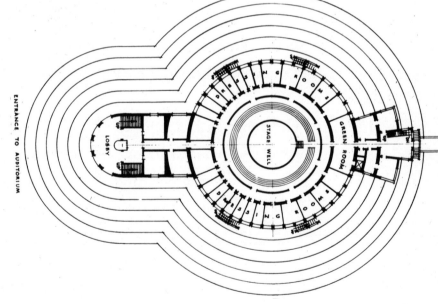

obviously, the purpose for which they are intended. Any one seeing these buildings or even examining photographs of them would realize that they were associated with the amusement industry.

129 · THEATER NUMBER 14: SECTION
DESIGNED BY NORMAN BEL GEDDES 1922

130 · THEATER NUMBER 14: BASEMENT PLAN
DESIGNED BY NORMAN BEL GEDDES 1922

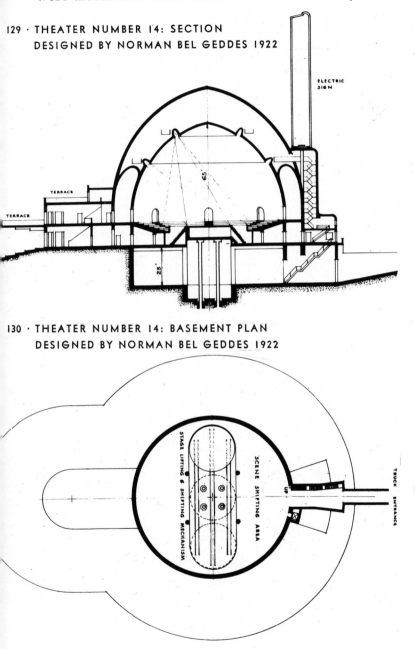

Theater Number 14,[126] is a small intimate theater, especially suited to intense dramatic plays of the close-up type such as those of Ibsen. It is designed on the same principle as a European circus or a boxing ring, with the stage in the center of the building.[127] The audience surrounds the stage. Separating the stage from the auditorium is a pit in which there are steps[127] forming an approach for actors to the stage.

This circular auditorium has no balcony and is only six rows deep. Because each seat commands an equally good view of the entire stage and is equally " the best in the house," the revenue from these eight hundred seats, all at the " top price," is equal to twice that number at the usual " sliding scale."

Surrounding the dome which spans both stage and auditorium are two concentric light galleries with locations for lamps at any conceivable angle.[129] All lamp positions are invisible to the seated audience during the performance. Inside the circular railing in front of the first row of seats is a row of lamps for throwing the light upward (as footlights do on a proscenium stage). The overhead light comes from an angle of forty-five degrees, which is the most favorable light for facial expression. All lamps are controlled from a single switchboard.

Surrounding the auditorium is a broad promenade with windows.[127] Projecting from the promenade is an upstairs lounge. On either side of this are retiring rooms for men and women and an outdoor terrace on the cantilevered marquee.[129]

The ground floor consists of entrance foyer,[128] box offices, manager's office, producer's offices, and assembly room for actors in conjunction with dressing rooms and stage, stage director's offices, stage manager's offices, stage-door foyer and waiting room, and the freight elevator entrance. The dressing rooms are under the auditorium on the ground floor.[128] Each has a bath, a shower and an outside window. These rooms radiate from a passage around the stairs that lead to the stage.

In this theater, scenery would be restricted to what is commonly termed properties, that is, objects such as furniture, and to skeleton constructions. Storage space for scenery and properties is provided in the basement.[130] All scene changes are made in the basement under the stage. The scenery is set on two movable platforms in the basement, which are raised and lowered by hydraulic power.[129] When raised, one platform forms the stage floor. Meanwhile, the other is being " set." These platforms can be used alternately and the substitution of one for the other requires only thirty seconds.

Many theaters in other eras have been more flexible and have offered greater possibilities for variety to both the dramatist and the producer than the proscenium-type stage of to-day. To test the principle of theater Number 14, you need only to put a wrestling match or boxing bout on the stage of a theater and see how tame it is in comparison with the effect it gives in the middle of an arena, with the audience surrounding it. The same thing can be achieved with a play.

The obvious criticism that might arise on inspecting the plans for theater Number 14 is the thought that the actor will always have his back to some part of the auditorium. This is true. But the proportion of time that the actor has his back turned towards any portion of the auditorium is no greater than the present practice with the proscenium stage. Furthermore, this auditorium is so small and so proportioned that a voice will be clearly heard in all parts of the auditorium, regardless of the direction the actor faces.

To illustrate my contention, I have selected the most difficult staging situation in any play that I know — the scene in " King Lear " where Lear is dividing his kingdom among his three daughters. I have made a drawing to illustrate this situation.[1] Lear has his back to the part of the auditorium from which the drawing is made. Let us assume that on a proscenium stage he would face the audience; then the three daughters would have their backs to

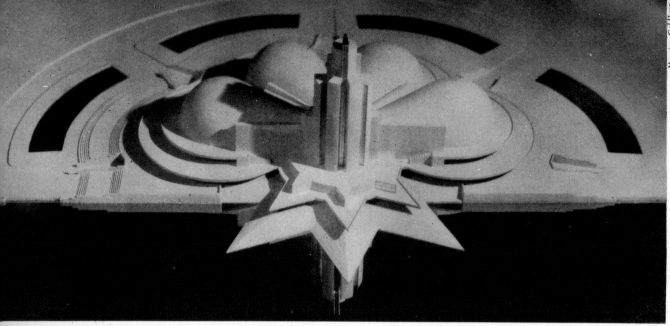

132 · TEMPLE OF MUSIC   DESIGNED BY NORMAN BEL GEDDES 1929

the audience or they would stand at one side, which would be unnatural, un-dramatic, and unconvincing. What appears, therefore, to be the worst posi-tion, that of Lear with his back to the audience, is best, for in this particular situation it is more important for the audience to see the expressions and reactions of the three daughters than of their father. But, with the audience on all sides of the stage, half of them do see the king's face at this moment.

On the stage of this theater, the action can be so directed that any impor-tant actor need have his back to no one part of the audience more than one eighth of the time. It is no more difficult to accomplish this than it is on the present stage to keep actors always facing the audience. It never occurs to us to criticize a boxing bout, a baseball game, a six-day bicycle race, the circus, or a cabaret performance because part of the time the protagonist has his back to us. A stage of this type would have a strong tendency to restore one of the great arts of the theater which has been almost entirely lost — pantomime.

The Temple of Music[132] was intended not only as a building for the Expo-sition but as a permanent structure for Chicago itself. The auditorium is suitable for symphony orchestras, choral festivals, and small chamber concerts. It is so designed that it complies with the two extremes of seating an audience: ten thousand persons listening to two hundred musicians and six hundred singers, or for use as a chamber concert hall to accommodate an audience of only eight hundred persons and a string quartet.

The stage, as fully extended, is a semicircle sixty-four feet in diameter, topped by a half dome. The auditorium is built in four sectional units without columns or balconies to impair the view or acoustics from any seat.[136] The walls and ceiling of each section form a dome which can be rolled back on itself, throwing the building open to the stars on a summer evening. Collapsible partitions permit variations in the size of the hall to meet different requirements. The necessary box offices and lounges are provided for each of the four sections.[135] Entrance foyers open onto a common terrace seventy-two feet wide. Two additional exterior promenades open off of upper levels.[133] A two hundred and fifty-six foot tower houses rehearsal rooms, studios, carillons, dressing rooms, and offices. Beneath the auditorium and terrace, a basement gives entrance and parking space for seventeen hundred and twenty automobiles.[134] There is additional parking space adjacent to each entrance of the building. Four lanes through the basement are so regulated that they

133 · TEMPLE OF MUSIC   DESIGNED BY NORMAN BEL GEDDES 1929

Maurice Goldberg

easily take care of incoming and outgoing traffic. At the four entrances, one hundred cars per minute can be unloaded.

There are four main entrances to the Temple of Music. The one you use is determined by the number on your ticket. These four entrance foyers are circular.[135] If you wish to go directly to your seat, and it is in the lower part of the auditorium, you walk almost in a straight line from the entrance door into the auditorium. If your seat is in the upper part of the auditorium, you go up circular stairs

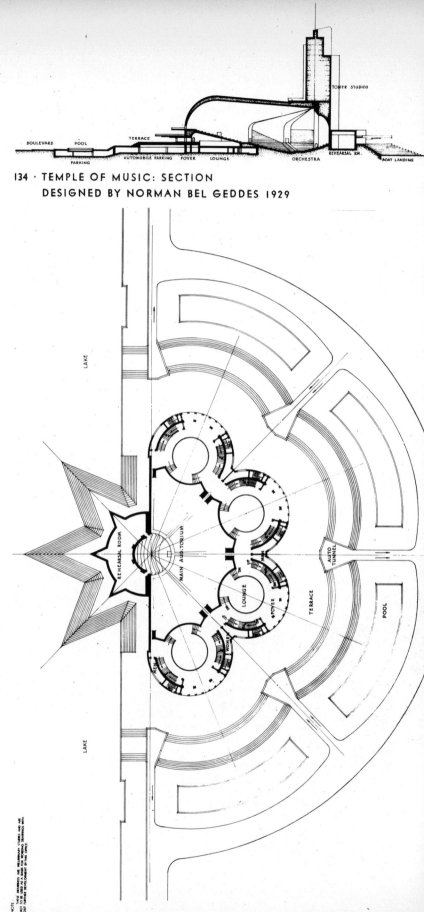

134 · TEMPLE OF MUSIC: SECTION
DESIGNED BY NORMAN BEL GEDDES 1929

135 · TEMPLE OF MUSIC: ENTRANCE FLOOR PLAN
DESIGNED BY NORMAN BEL GEDDES 1929

to the higher level. If you wish to wait for some one before taking your seat, you go down a few steps into a circular lounge that accommodates three hundred persons. Here you can wait in comfort for your friends, who upon entering, can easily locate you, as the lounge is in the center of and below the rest of the foyer.

This building is designed entirely for musical entertainment, not for dramatic productions. An outstanding feature of the auditorium is its division into four sub-elements[136] which eliminate the vast armory-like or exposition hall characteristic of a building seating ten thousand persons in a single mass on one floor. Sitting within any one of the four circular wings of this auditorium, a person can view at the most only about one half of the auditorium's total seating capacity and yet see the full stage.

This building was originally planned for the Chicago lake front where it was adjacent to many suburbs by motor boat. For persons arriving by boat there are three landing docks at the star point base of the tower.[132]

The Water Pageant Theater is designed as a series of anchored barges in a lagoon or lake within a public park.[137] The barges are locked together in varying combinations and the combination is changed as desired. It is for the use of spec-

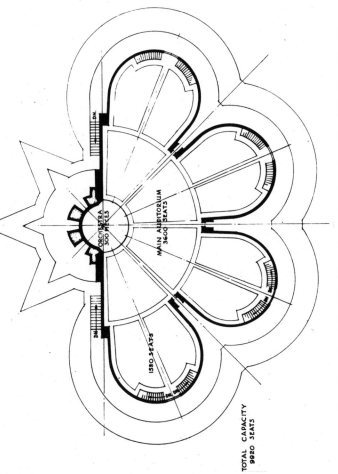

137 · WATER PAGEANT THEATER   DESIGNED BY NORMAN BEL GEDDES 1929

tacular pageants, pantomimes, choral festivals and orchestral concerts. It is
an open air theater for summer evening use only.

The auditorium proper seats two thousand persons. Separating the auditorium section from the stage is a canal, permitting watercraft to take part
in the pageants. A portion of the canal is roped off for four hundred canoes.
The fifteen hundred occupants of these have the choice seats and watch the
performance without landing.[138] At either end of this canal are traffic towers
to control the movements of the canoes. The auditorium is divided into four
main sections. There are five aisles and a promenade at the back of each section. The two side sections rise above the water level from four to thirteen
feet, and the two center sections rise from four to twenty-two feet. In the
rear of each section are wide flights of stairs leading from the landings to the
highest level. To the sides and rear of the auditorium are radiating piers sup-

plying docks for seven hundred and sixty-eight small boats simultaneously.[138]

The stage consists of a series of platforms, and likewise built on barges, connected by stairs and under passages. Starting at eight inches above the water, these platforms build up to a height of thirty-six feet. Above are towers and a wall which serve as the background for the stage and eliminate the necessity for scenery. The stage is illuminated by flood lights situated at the rear of the auditorium and by side lights concealed on the stage group of barges, and by other lights concealed on the stage itself. Auditorium aisles are illuminated by lights at the ends of the seats on each row. General illumination for the auditorium is from flood lights located both at the rear of the auditorium and on the stage. These latter may, as required, serve as a "blinder" replacing the conventional curtain. The irregular shape of the stage, together with its numerous levels, permit variety in stage direction and

138 · WATER PAGEANT THEATER: PLAN   DESIGNED BY NORMAN BEL GEDDES 1929

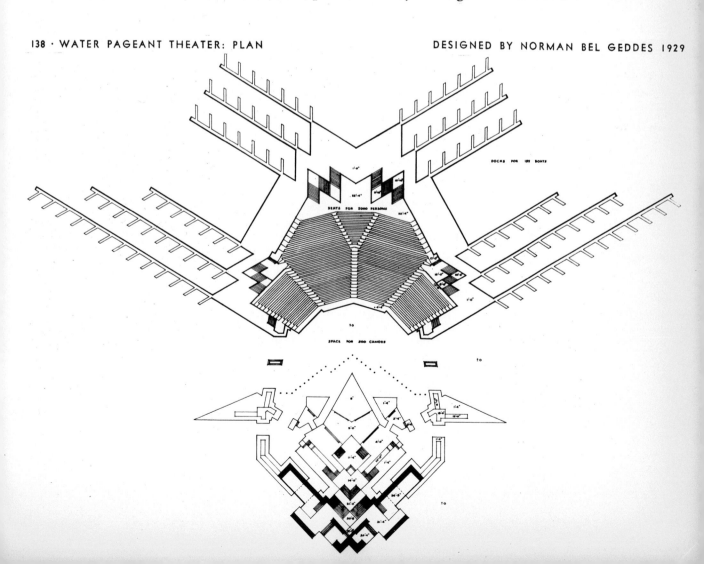

Maurice Goldberg

in the ensemble movement. Underneath the high portion of the stage, in addition to property rooms and offices, are three floors of dressing rooms for actors, providing sixteen single dressing rooms for principals with a shower bath for each pair of rooms. Six dressing rooms accommodate a chorus of two hundred and sixteen with toilets and showers adjoining. There are four actors' assembly rooms between the dressing rooms and entrances to the stage.

The water pageant theater with its docks and canals is 468 feet on the longitudinal axis and 632 feet at its widest point. The auditorium is 112 feet deep at the center and 294 feet wide at its greatest spread. The distance from the point of the apron to the rear of the stage towers is 172 feet; and from wall to wall the stage measures 161 feet. The towers at the back of the stage are 80 feet high. The average width of the canal dividing the acting area of the stage from the auditorium is 135 feet.

The stage is so designed and so variable in form that it serves the requirements of any kind of mass production — dramatic and musical. It would be ideal for reviving the glorious old pageants such as were given in the days of the Italian Renaissance, when Leonardo Da Vinci designed them. Ballets mirroring themselves in the water would be a spectacle to hold any audience. The particular requirement for the effectiveness of such a theater is an appropriate setting in a large park with a body

140 · UKRAINIAN STATE THEATER: DESIGNED BY NORMAN BEL GEDDES 1931

of water sufficient to set it off, and the right person as its directing head.

In 1931 I was invited by the United States of Soviet Russia to enter their competition for The Ukrainian State Theater to be built at Karkov. This building has as its outstanding feature a façade which becomes the stage for a great mass production,[139] with the plaza in front of the building serving as the auditorium. This arrangement was not stipulated in the specifications provided by the Russian Government, but was the result of another idea which they imposed. They required a rostrum from which speakers could address sixty thousand persons assembled in the square. I designed this and, as permitted in the terms of the competition, went further, supplying a stage on which five thousand actors might play for the same audience. The building combines three complete theaters, the Indoor Theater, an Open-Air Theater on the roof, and the Outdoor Mass Theater. In addition, there are complete workshops,[140] rehearsal rooms, storages, offices, and social and dressing quarters for a large acting company.

The outstanding feature of the design of the Indoor Theater, so far as the

[173]

convenience of the audience is concerned, is the means by which crowds, when entering or leaving, are handled. All vehicular traffic at the front of the theater is underground to facilitate movement and to eliminate the possibility of injury to pedestrians. The parking area under the plaza accommodates six hundred and fifty automobiles. The plan for entrance and exit is worked out strictly for one-way traffic. There are facilities for unloading fifty automobiles per minute within the building itself. Four hundred persons a minute can enter the building and walk directly to their seats without crossing each other's path. Facilities for checking hats and overcoats, located directly opposite each main stairway in the main vestibule, are on the line of entrance and exit of every person, and the longest time any one person should require for checking or obtaining wraps is one minute.

The indoor auditorium accommodates four thousand persons. The seats are arranged in three tiers, with no balcony.[144] The three tiers are reached from either the ground floor or from the foyer by twelve entrance doors on each level.[141] There is a system of stairways from the vestibule to the foyer and from the backs of the lower and middle tiers to the fronts of the middle and upper tiers. The foyer,[146] located above the main vestibule, has an area of twenty-one thousand three hundred square feet and is thirty-eight feet in height. It affords access to the middle and upper tiers of seats in the auditorium and to the restaurant and refreshment bar located in front of the theater building.[144]

Four boxes are provided in the first two rows of the middle tier for the use of visiting diplomats and societies.[144] They may be reached from the ground floor or foyer levels. Private reception rooms are adjacent to these boxes in the foyer.

All auditorium lighting is indirect, being accomplished by flood lights placed in the recesses of the ceiling which follow in plan the curve of the seats.[142] Above and behind these ceiling recesses are located spot lights and bridges for illumination of the stage.[143] The main light bridge is located above and in front of the proscenium. Cinema galleries with attendant rooms are provided in the space above the foyer and behind the auditorium.

142 · UKRAINIAN STATE THEATER: AUDITORIUM   DESIGNED BY NORMAN BEL GEDDES 1931

The stage mechanical equipment is of the most advanced order. The proscenium opening is designed so that it can be reduced or enlarged for any size of scene — for a scene with three persons or a scene with a thousand.[143] The arch may be expanded from its minimum width of opening, 27 feet, to a maximum width of 196 feet. The height may vary from a minimum of 16 feet to a maximum of 58 feet, at which point stage and auditorium would be one. The change is accomplished without in any way sacrificing the visibility of the audience and may be made during performances.

The stage floor is composed of five units:[146] Main Stage, fore-stage, and rear stage, all of which are supported on hydraulic plungers, and the right and left proscenium stages, which are stationary.[145] Under ordinary circumstances, the fore-stage will be used by the orchestra or as the front auditorium seating section. It may be raised from the level of the upper basement to either the auditorium or stage level.[143] Or it may remain at a level below the auditorium floor, be set with steps and become a lower fore-stage — permitting actors to enter from underneath the audience.[142] The stage organism has been so designed that the entire stage floor is exclusively the actors' realm; all scenery being pre-set on the movable stages at the basement level.[145] The movable stages are operated from a control room located under the left proscenium stage. From his station the operator can watch the progress of the play, the shifting of all scenery in the basement, in the " flies ", and on the stage proper. All stage units are " trapped " over their entire area. The exits from the traps are adjacent to the upper basement level.[145]

The permanent cyclorama extends around the entire stage[144] and from the stage floor to the underside of the gridiron.[143] It is of soundproof construction, excluding all exterior and " offstage " noise. It is lighted from the light pit (upper basement level) which extends around the rear of the rear stage, or from above. The gridiron is designed to permit not only the flying of scenery,

[176]

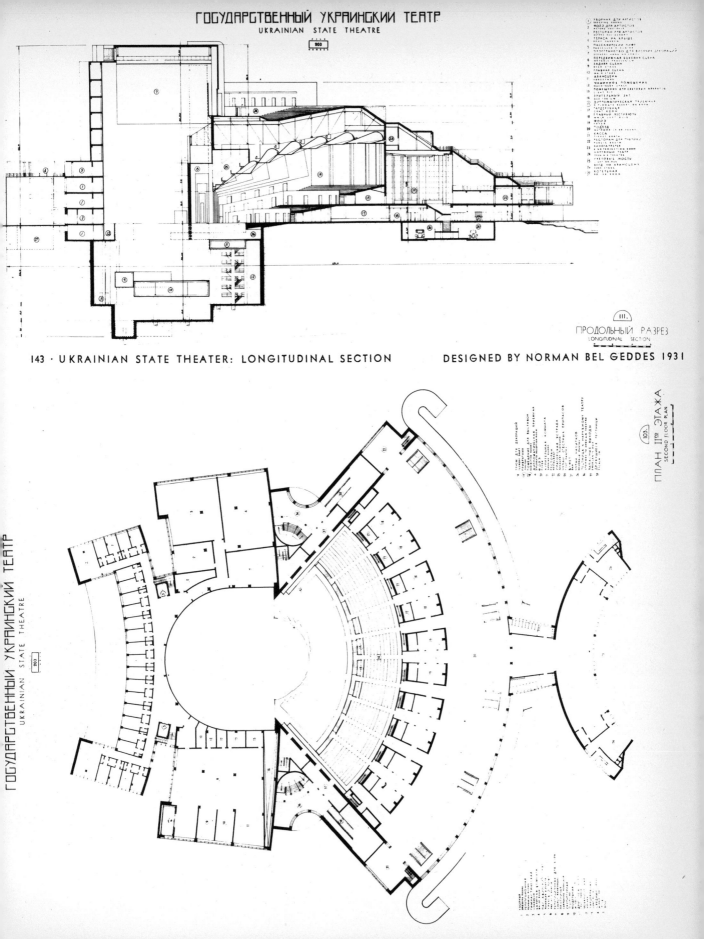

ГОСУДАРСТВЕННЫЙ УКРАИНСКИЙ ТЕАТР
UKRAINIAN STATE THEATRE

ПРОДОЛЬНЫЙ РАЗРЕЗ
LONGITUDINAL SECTION

143 · UKRAINIAN STATE THEATER: LONGITUDINAL SECTION   DESIGNED BY NORMAN BEL GEDDES 1931

ГОСУДАРСТВЕННЫЙ УКРАИНСКИЙ ТЕАТР
UKRAINIAN STATE THEATRE

ПЛАН II^го ЭТАЖА
SECOND FLOOR PLAN

144 · UKRAINIAN STATE THEATER: AUDITORIUM FLOOR PLAN   DESIGNED BY NORMAN BEL GEDDES 1931

but the hanging of several productions at one time, as well as automatic storage of unused scenery in a fire-proof enclosure at either side of the stage.[145] In a repertory schedule this eliminates the necessity of dismantling one production to replace with another between performances. It permits of interchanging scenery in the flies during a performance. The gridiron accommodates one hundred and sixty sets of lines, each set being so arranged that it travels from a position over the stage to the scenery-storing space at either side. Furthermore, the gridiron extends out over the apron section, in front of the proscenium, which is a distinct innovation.[143] When scenery for a particular scene is removed from the stage — instead of being raised into the flies after the performance, it will again be lowered to the stage, wrapped up and sent to storage — by this mechanism; upon reaching the flies, it may be automatically transported to the fireproof storage section in another part of the building. In the side spaces of the stage, commonly spoken of as the "wings", are large assembly rooms located on both sides of and adjacent to the stage. These waiting rooms are for waiting actors, and for stage managers to order and check crowds of five hundred actors with their properties, prior to their entrance onto the stage.[146] These two rooms are directly accessible to all dressing rooms by means of stairways and large passenger elevators. They are separated from the stage by soundproof vestibules and may be used for rehearsal space.

It is possible to join any and all parts of this auditorium directly with the stage.[143] When so arranged, actors and audience may walk directly on to any part of the stage from any part of the auditorium. That portion of the stage which extends into the auditorium and is known as the apron can project varying distances, up to a maximum of fifty feet beyond the proscenium line, by merely pressing a button at the stage control board.

Processes involved in the manufacture of scenery are provided for on the basis of single line operation. After being built in the carpenter shop, scenery is lifted by elevator to the painting shop. Upon completion of painting, the scenery is lifted to the storage rooms.[145] From storage, the scenery is transported directly to the stage. All scenery workshops are located on the right side of the stage, one above another. Costume cutting, sewing, fitting, and storage rooms are on the left side of the stage.[145] The concentration of workshops in one location is consistent with modern methods of production in the movement of work from one department

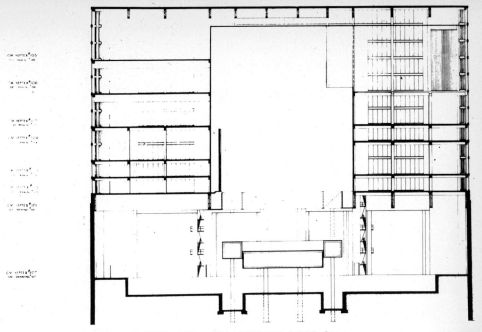

145 · UKRAINIAN STATE THEATER: TRANSVERSE SECTION
DESIGNED BY NORMAN BEL GEDDES 1931

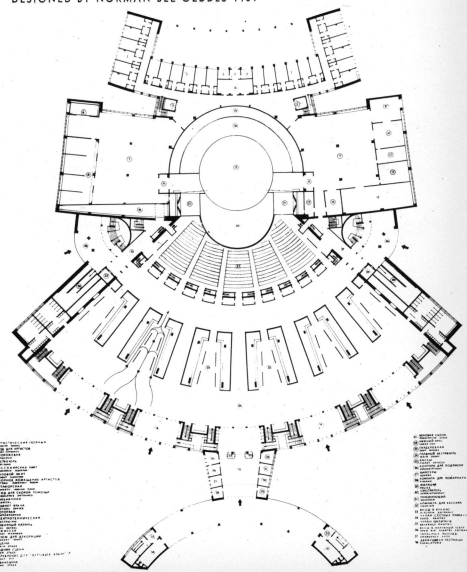

146 · UKRAINIAN STATE THEATER: GROUND FLOOR PLAN
DESIGNED BY NORMAN BEL GEDDES 1931

to another. The maximum of natural light is provided, as all workshop walls, exterior and interior, are entirely of glass.[140]

Actors' quarters, including dressing rooms, social rooms, restaurant, and library are located in the building directly behind the stage.[146] These quarters, without regard for precedent, are as comfortable as they can be made. The individual dressing rooms for all major members of the company number over a hundred, all of which are as comfortable as a room with a bath in a modern hotel.

On the roof is an Open-Air Theater seating two thousand persons.[139] The open-air theater is in direct communication with the street by escalators on either side of the building,[146] making it unnecessary to enter the structure to reach it. On the other hand, it is also in direct communication with the indoor theater. The same dressing rooms function for the main theater and for the roof theater. On either side of the open-air roof theater are two large enclosed foyers for use in the event of sudden rain. The open-air theater is designed for the presentation of plays and concerts and for public assemblies not in excess of two thousand persons.

The Outdoor Mass Theater accommodates an audience of sixty thousand persons who may be seated or standing in the plaza upon which the building faces.[139] The entire facade of the building is designed for the use of its exterior form as a tremendous stage.[143] Five thousand actors at one time can perform on it and be clearly visible to the entire audience.

Powerful flood lights and sound amplifiers located in the six pylons or towers which stand in the plaza furnish illumination for the facade of the building and amplify any sound which may occur upon it.[139] They also furnish general illumination for the plaza. A speaker's platform is located at the foyer level in front of the restaurant facing the plaza. With the assistance of the sound-amplification system located in the six pylons, the speaker, without raising his voice, can be heard by the entire audience. Access to the Mass Stage is obtained from the Open-Air Roof Theater and it is connected with the plaza by means of stairs, ramps and an exterior promenade which extends around the front of the theater at the foyer level and which also serves as the audience's main exit from the foyer level."[139]

There is no question in my mind but that theater architecture will break away from the antiquated proscenium formula. The motion picture is helping it along. By its technique, it affords immensely diversified entertainment which, except for the fact that the medium is frankly two-dimensional, can give us a sense of all outdoors or, on the other hand, the most intimate corner of a room. This medium is much more flexible than the present proscenium acting stage, which is the most limiting form the stage has ever had. Consequently, I feel certain that the theater and cinema will grow farther and farther apart as time goes on — to the advantage of both.

The cinema, as it grows up, will become a much more distinct medium than it is at present. Just now it is in a state of transition, reflecting and using talent and ideas straight from the theater. Ten years hence, moving-picture technique will have progressed to such a degree that screen presentations will be scarcely recognizable in comparison with offerings to-day. It will be found that the cinema can do everything that can be done upon the proscenium type of stage. This is the best thing that could happen to the stage, because the theater will then fall back upon its own special facilities. These facilities are primarily of a three-dimensional order.

CHAPTER 9

Restaurant Architecture

Francis Bruguiere

Nine years ago Morris Gest engaged me to design the production of the Miracle for Max Reinhardt at the Century Theater, New York. Mr. Reinhardt had produced the Miracle many times, and he wanted me to work out an idea for presenting the play that would be different from any he had used before. The scheme that was finally evolved was to reconstruct the interior of the theater into a cathedral.

The large proscenium of the Century Theater was thrown open to its full width and height. The stage became the apse and the auditorium itself took on the appearance of a transept. As you entered the rear of the auditorium, you had the sense of standing in the nave and looking through the transept into the

[182]

148 · CENTURY THEATER AUDITORIUM: THE MIRACLE
DESIGNED BY NORMAN BEL GEDDES 1924

apse. To accomplish this result, the entire auditorium as well as the stage was completely covered with architectural scenery.[149] The scenery was not painted on canvas but was built of wood and covered with a material which, to the touch as well as to the sight, was stone.[147] The aisles were covered with rectangular pieces of asbestos slate which, under foot, sounded and looked like stone. The seats were converted into pews. The boxes on each side of the auditorium were removed and rebuilt into cloisters.[148] But the feature that really achieved the result was the manner in which the whole structure was illuminated; or perhaps it should be stated in the opposite: the manner in which it was *not* illuminated. Except for the tremendous light that came through the

[183]

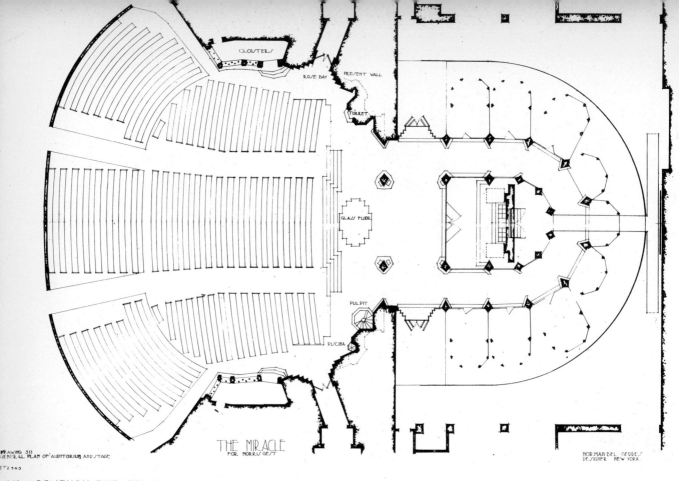

THE MIRACLE
FOR MORRIS GEST

DRAWING 511
GENERAL PLAN OF AUDITORIUM AND STAGE

NORMAN DEL GEDDES
DESIGNER NEW YORK

149 · CENTURY THEATER PLAN: THE MIRACLE   DESIGNED BY NORMAN BEL GEDDES 1924

enormous stained-glass windows (eighty feet high) at the sides of the transept and around the apse, there was scarcely any illumination at all. The
entire structure was painted dull black. Consequently, you had the feeling of
being in the musty dark atmosphere of an old continental cathedral.[147]

As a result of this setting, moving-picture theaters all over the country
were redecorated to resemble cathedrals, Chinese pagodas, Egyptian temples,
Spanish courtyards and the like. Then the movement spread to restaurants.
When I refused to accept a commission to design several restaurants for a
woman, now well known in the field, she used my name, until I had to take
legal action against her to prevent the implication that I had designed her
restaurants which were in imitation of my treatment of the Century Theater. Later, even the Child's restaurant which for years had maintained a

style that was well known and recognized instantly the country over, changed a number of its establishments into Old English taverns. The point of view that has faith in creating a fake atmosphere is all too typically American. At the Chicago World's Fair of 1893, architects built Grecian temples in the form of business buildings, and since then they have imitated every known architectural style in Europe for one purpose or another.

In the case of the Miracle it is a different story. Architecture is one thing, scenery is another. The story of this play took place in a church of the Middle Ages. In order to stage the play, it was necessary to create the atmosphere for it. To be sure, it could have been done in an abstract style and in fact I endeavored to persuade Reinhardt to do it in such a way, but this is beside the point. What we did was thoroughly dignified and appropriate.

In Coney Island and California we often see an entire shop built as a sign for its wares. An ice-cream cone is sold in a shop whose architectural form resembles a milk can[150] or an ice-cream freezer, with a long swinging crank to attract attention. The soda fountain is buried under a mountain of imitation-stucco snow. Soft drinks are imbibed at counters set inside of immense barrels, or at booths shaped like oranges or lemons. The architectural form of the Brown Derby Restaurant does everything possible to resemble a huge bowler.

Such innovations are, of course, merely applications of advertising principles to architecture. As a genre, the result might be known as Coney Island Architecture. But it is symptomatic and interesting on that account. Unquestionably, a new liveliness is coming into

150 · THE CREAM CAN   DESIGNER UNKNOWN

Keystone View

151 · OPEN AIR CABARET   DESIGNED BY NORMAN BEL GEDDES 1929

architecture and we may yet hear of it as one of the Seven Lively Arts. It can certainly be made as vivacious as the tabloids, the talkies, or vaudeville. But there is another type of building, less obvious, and dignified enough to be classed as architecture.

A sincere style in architecture is the direct result of the problem to be solved, of the materials involved, and of the sensitiveness of the artist. An artificial style is applied decoration. At present, the country is flooded with a great quantity of examples of the poor under the pseudonym of the "modern*istic* style." The italics are mine. The *istics* like the *isms* are fussers, gadgeteers, pseudo-artists. But the public is learning to differentiate between work that is merely craftsmanship without good design and that which is at least well designed and perhaps a work of art; between the mere craft of building and a building by an artist which becomes architecture. The exterior

[186]

form of such architecture grows out of its inner purpose, and its character-istics are in keeping with its purpose. Novel amusement buildings, with higher claims to consideration as architecture than the obvious derby-hat restaurant may well become a commonplace in the future.

At strategic positions throughout the exhibition grounds of any big fair enterprise, there must be located large restaurant areas to handle scores of thousands of persons, who desire to eat at approximately the same hours. The

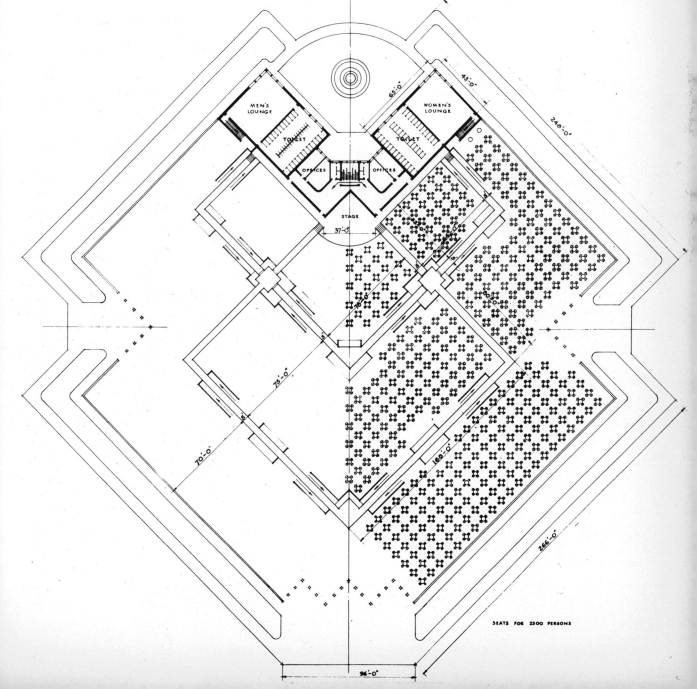

SEATS FOR 2500 PERSONS

success of the entire fair may depend upon the facility with which the hungry crowds are accommodated; and, to some extent, the success of the fair may depend upon maintaining the festal character of the enterprise throughout the dining period. Restaurant architecture to meet these conditions must be not only practical from the cooking and serving points of view; it must also be inviting because of its novelty, and if it offers certain amusement features, so much the better.

The Open-Air Cabaret[151] was the outgrowth of the particular problems that I have just indicated. Here is an eating place at a low price for a large number of patrons, and comparable in American terms to the sidewalk cafés of France and the beer gardens of Germany. The open-air cabaret seats 2,250 persons. To merely build a fence around the area and put the diners inside

153 · ISLAND DANCE RESTAURANT   DESIGNED BY NORMAN BEL GEDDES 1924

would be as appetizing as Chicago's famous stockyards, but less remunerative. Consequently, the space has been broken up into units, by low-walled hedges. Each unit is built on a slightly different level. There is a satisfactory psychological reaction in going up or down a few steps and passing into another

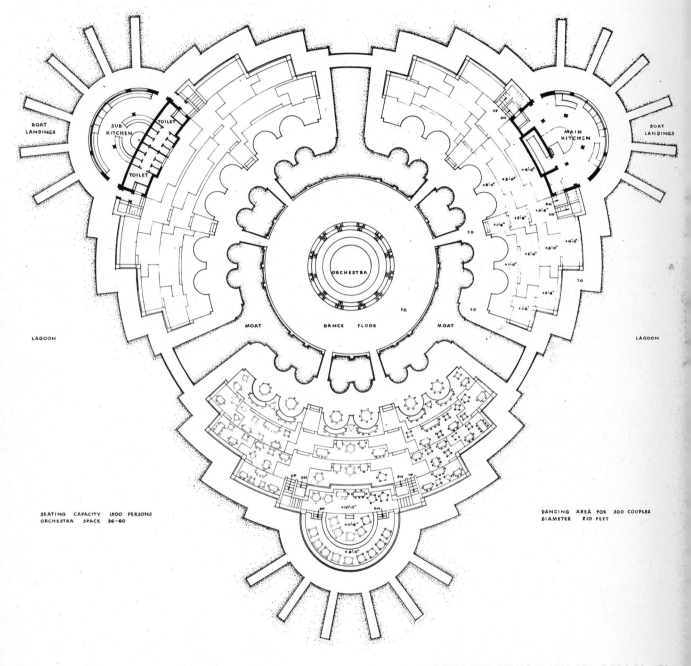

DESIGNED BY NORMAN BEL GEDDES 1924

space that adds variety and detracts from the monotony of an enormous area.

These walls are so designed that they are used as passages for waiters and busboys.[152] Any waiter or busboy travels eighty per cent of the distance from the kitchen to any table, out of sight of the diners. The tops of these walled passages are used as the apron of the stage. (The apron is the part of a stage that projects into the auditorium.) A performer can leave the stage as he starts to sing a song, or juggle an egg, or do sleight-of-hand, or a tap dance, or whatever his act happens to be, and finish long before he has made a complete circuit of the various ramifications of this apron stage. In this way the entertainment is brought into more intimate contact with the audience and offers continuous variety. Half a dozen acts can be going on simultaneously without interfering with one another. The different levels into which the restaurant is divided not only give variety, but increase the visibility and sight lines. They make it possible for persons sitting at the far end of the garden to see the stage and performers in all other parts of the garden.

Its three-story building contains lounges for men and women, offices, dressing rooms for entertainers, rooms for electricians and mechanics, kitchens and pantries.[152] Directly in front of the building is the small quadrant-shaped stage from which run the covered passageways at an average height of four feet above the ground-floor level, in the form of two interlacing squares. The sides of the passageways are walled up and their intersections enlarged to form sub-pantries. Ramps lead to the passageways from the floor level of the dining areas.[152] The sinking of the passages for waiters below the level of the ground keeps the waiters from obstructing the view of those watching the entertainment and keeps food and dishes out of sight most of the time. The farthest point any diner is removed from the meandering stage is a depth of five tables or the equivalent of about twelve rows in a theater.[151]

Surrounding the whole cabaret are steps, with entrances on the four main axes. The entrance gates are high grilles made of Neon tubes supported on duraluminum frames.[151] The plot of ground is approximately four hundred feet square. Of this area, seven thousand square feet are taken up by the entrance building, and sixty-five thousand square feet by chairs and tables.

I have indicated that restaurant architecture should comprise features which in themselves are capable of furnishing amusement. From this viewpoint, consider the Island Dance Restaurant. Here is an open-air restaurant in the middle of a lagoon.[152] Although it seats an enormous number of people, it is so broken up in plan that it does not appear as vast as it is in reality. It offers continuously varying interest, due to the fact that it *is* broken up: canoes floating about on all sides, couples dancing on a circular floor around the orchestra, the dancers mirrored in the water. Thirty-six slender Neon tubes spring from the orchestra floor and unite in a series of interlacing arches, which are the main source of illumination.[153] The tubes are supported on light duraluminum frames. The inner circle, which is on the outer edge of the orchestra platform turns slowly at the rate of one revolution in five minutes. These tubes would not only light the restaurant and the central area of the Exposition grounds but would be the largest beacon in the world and visible for a great distance. Neon tubes do not heat, so the dancing couples could not burn themselves.

This restaurant is a group of four islands.[154] Three small canals radiate from the inner lagoon that encircles the dance floor, joining it with the main outer lagoon. These entrance canals divide the dining terraces into three sections. It is possible for canoes to enter from the main lagoon and circle the dance floor without disturbing dancers or diners. These three sections comprise the dining area. The restaurant has space for an orchestra of thirty pieces

[191]

in the center. The dance floor comfortably accommodates two hundred couples. It completely surrounds the orchestra and is separated from the dining terraces by a canal fourteen feet wide. Six bridges span this canal, leading from the dining terraces to the dance floor, eliminating the usual congestion and the possibility of crowding tables for late comers onto the dance floor.

The terraces provide a table area for eight hundred diners. The terraces radiate from the dance floor and rise at the rear to twelve feet above the water level. The terrace arrangement permits the entire dance floor to be visible

155 · AQUARIUM RESTAURANT   DESIGNED BY NORMAN BEL GEDDES 1929

from every table. Each of the three dining islands has a semicircular landing platform with radiating docks for small water craft. Each island has its own ladies' and gentlemen's retiring rooms underneath the higher terraces. One of the sections houses the main kitchen. The other two sections house sub-kitchens and serving pantries. Steam trucks convey cooked food from the main kitchen to the sub-kitchens.

[192]

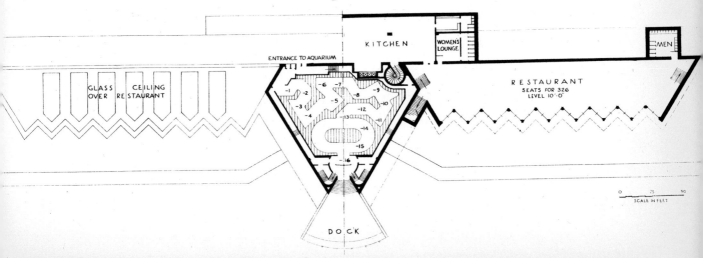

The area covered by the Island Dance Restaurant is approximately 566,000 square feet, of which 10,000 square feet are devoted to the orchestra; 30,400 square feet are devoted to the dance floor, and 136,280 square feet to the dining terraces.

The grounds for the Chicago Exposition are mostly filled in. In the original program it was the intention to utilize and feature Lake Michigan and the lagoons as much as possible. The Aquarium Restaurant is an underwater eating place suitable only for Fair or amusement grounds where expense is no particular object, providing a unique result is obtained. It was designed to be built across a lagoon where it forms a dam, for the water to flow over.[155] The building consists of a triangular shaped aquarium in the center with a restaurant to each side of the aquarium and joining it with the shores.

The entrance to the aquarium is by a dock at the lower water level.[156] This entrance dock is reached by boats from either shore.[157] A trip through the aquarium is planned to give the visitor the feeling of having made a journey to the bottom of the sea. The interior walls, floor and ceiling are glass tanks containing underwater plant and animal life. Thus the tanks are above, below, and on all sides. The arrangement creates the illusion that any one passing through the building, instead of looking at tanks containing fish, is himself *within* the tank with the fish on the outside all around him.

The passage between the tanks is a circuitous maze[157] that gradually ramps downward. All illumination comes through the water. Near the surface, this is the warm color of water permeated with sunlight. Gradually, as one descends, the color deepens, and deep-sea life appears in place of shallow-water creatures.

The exterior walls of the building, over which falls a curtain of water, are illuminated by invisible lights underneath the water. On the roof of the aquarium is an open-air terrace (one hundred feet at its widest point and ninety-five feet on its longest axis) with a seating capacity for one hundred and twenty persons. It is reached from the restaurant and has its own pantry unit. Water flows underneath its glass floor and in a curtain over the walls of the terrace.

The restaurant is in two sections, one on either side of the aquarium.[157] The ceiling is glass over which two inches of water flows; the wall along the front elevation is glass. The six-foot overhang of the roof throws the water out from the window in a thin, semi-transparent curtain.[156]

Another structure, having novelty of a different sort, is The Aërial Restaurant.[158] A casual observer inspecting these designs might assume that in its engineering and structural features, it is impractical. The facts are otherwise. While the shaft is thin in proportion to the whole mass, it is actually thirty-two feet wide. Though the upper structure appears to have more weight on one side than the other, the segments of the three cantilevered levels are actually so arranged that they balance on each side of the center with sufficient leeway to take care of all live loads.

The chief reason that brought about the designing of The Aërial Restaurant was its novelty to attract a repeat audience of Chicagoans themselves to the Exposition grounds. Another condition was that in the main part of the grounds, where the principal buildings were situated, there was no attractive space that could be set aside for large restaurants. Though this tower rises in the air over twenty stories, it does not use the ground space that would ordi-

Maurice Goldberg

DESIGNED BY NORMAN BEL GEDDES 1929

narily be required in order to attain the square foot area of the three floors.[159] Thirdly, the projected buildings up to that time lacked anything in the way of height for the purpose of solving the observation-tower problem.

In this structure, we have a building the base of which is so small it could be built within the courtyard of another building. Its main mass does not spread out until it has reached a considerable height above the ground. Hence it does not interfere with the two and three-story height of nearly all other

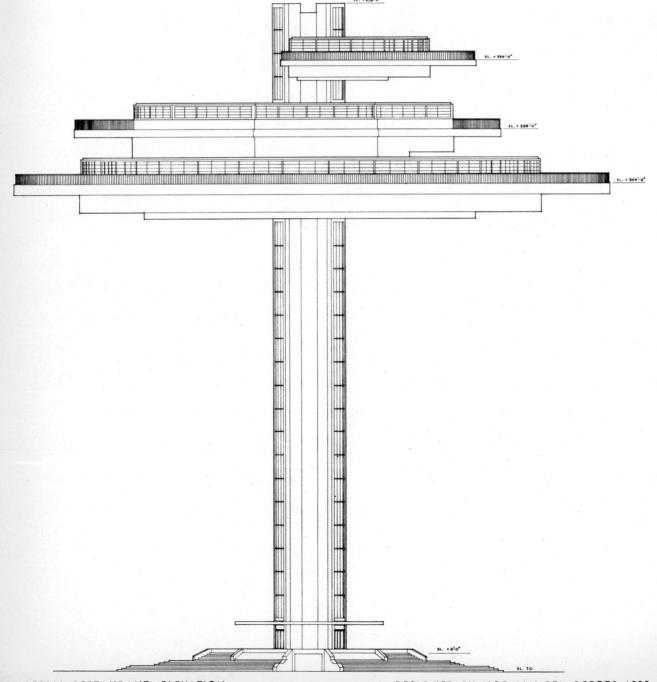

159 · AERIAL RESTAURANT: ELEVATION   DESIGNED BY NORMAN BEL GEDDES 1929

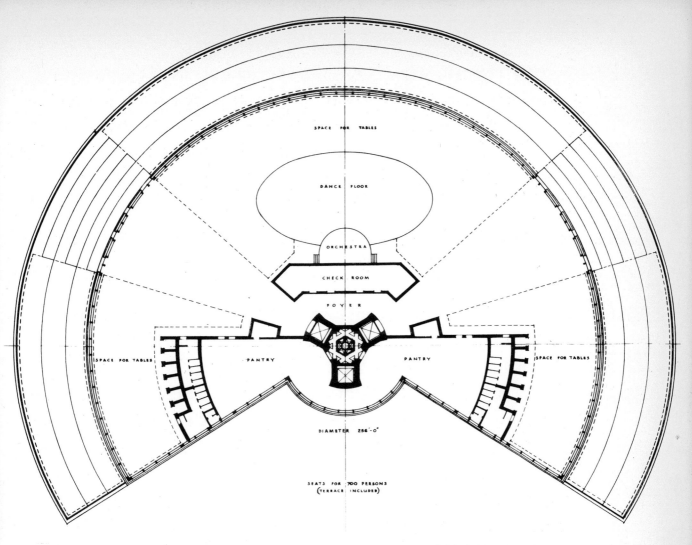

SPACE FOR TABLES

DANCE FLOOR

ORCHESTRA

CHECK ROOM

FOYER

SPACE FOR TABLES

PANTRY

PANTRY

SPACE FOR TABLES

DIAMETER 256'-0"

SEATS FOR 700 PERSONS
(TERRACE INCLUDED)

160 · AERIAL RESTAURANT: PLAN OF MAIN RESTAURANT LEVEL   DESIGNED BY NORMAN BEL GEDDES 1929

buildings proposed for the Fair. The Aërial Restaurant offers an observation platform with clear vision for miles around. It looks out over the lake and it looks out over the city. The building's greatest novelty is that the entire structure slowly revolves, so that during a meal restaurant patrons get two complete panoramic views of the Fair Grounds, the City of Chicago, and Lake Michigan from an elevation of twenty-seven stories. There are three restaurants on three different levels, with a seating capacity of fifteen hundred persons.

The entrance, on the ground level, is approached by a series of three circular terraces with steps.[158] From the top terrace are entrances, protected by a marquee, to three large elevators. Directly under the entrance terrace is the main kitchen, one story high and built above the ground level. For culinary deliveries, a ramped passageway leads to the kitchen. Below the kitchen is housed the heavy mechanism for revolving the upper part of the structure. The central shaft, in addition to three large elevators for patrons, contains nine service elevators. Due to the elevators stopping at only three levels, one hundred and seventy persons can enter or leave the building every five minutes.

Each of the three restaurants has glass walls from floor to ceiling and open-air terraces surrounding them. The first or main restaurant level has a seating capacity of seven hundred,[160] with a dance floor for two hundred and fifty couples and an orchestra space for twelve pieces. Two elevators lead to the foyer directly in front of which is a checkroom. Wide promenades lead from the foyer through the restaurant to three open-air terraces. The second or intermediate level is devoted solely to light refreshments and drinks at popular prices. It has a seating capacity of five hundred people. The third or top level of the Aërial Restaurant has a seating capacity of two hundred persons with great space and comfort. This is an eating place of an exclusive order, where the best food may be obtained at admittedly high prices.

I know of no restaurant in America or Europe which, to any major extent, resembles these I have described. Cabarets and other entertainments were introduced into restaurants some years ago as an added attraction and are now commonplace. I see no reason why architecture should not be utilized as an added attraction for the restaurant, if it can be interesting and so join in the spirit of the occasion.

Reduced in size, the Island Dance Restaurant and the Open-Air Cabaret are both applicable to a roof garden and could be made to furnish gorgeous diversion. The water in the lagoon for the Island Dance Restaurant would eliminate or reduce the size of the water tank necessary for additional fire protection on top of the building, if it were kept filled the year round. In the not too distant future I anticipate restaurants of this type in our larger cities attracting generous patronage. Up to the present moment, architects and public alike have shown no initiative or imagination in utilizing their roofs. Utilization of roof area will be one of the leading architectural developments of the next few years.

CHAPTER 10

What Price Factory Ugliness?

Ugliness, in varied forms, was the outstanding characteristic of the beginnings of the industrial age — exploitation of the workers, oppressive hours, inhumane conditions, dirt, poorly organized buildings. Factory existence was a nightmare. Gradually, throughout a half century, conditions improved. With this improvement came the recognition that light, cleanliness, ventilation, and even agreeable surroundings were advantageous not only to the employees but to the profits and peace of mind of the employers. As the dawn of modern factory architecture arrived, I hasten to add that the dawn's early gleams escaped the attention of the architects themselves.

Modern factory architecture is a product of engineering. The viewpoint of the engineer is in contrast with that of the architect. The engineer has been the dominant factor in building, during the last two generations. You read much of Gothic Architecture, and you should; nevertheless Gothic *engineering* made the architecture possible.

Gothic architects either were engineers or used engineers. Engineering is a science. Architecture is an art. Building itself is just a craft. When Michelangelo, generally thought of as a painter and sculptor,' conceived St. Peter's at Rome, he thought in terms of an engineer. But being an artist as well, the result was a work of architecture.[161]

Quite different was the attitude of our architects of the gay nineties. They were in their element in doing mausoleums, government buildings, and other examples of monumental architecture, but gave a factory no architectural ranking. A factory had to be built economically; wasn't supposed to be seen by anybody except the workers; there was no reason why a factory should have æsthetic appeal as it was merely a place for machines and for people to work who used machines. When architects did take a hand, it was mainly because of the remuneration, and without any consideration for the problems involved, they de-

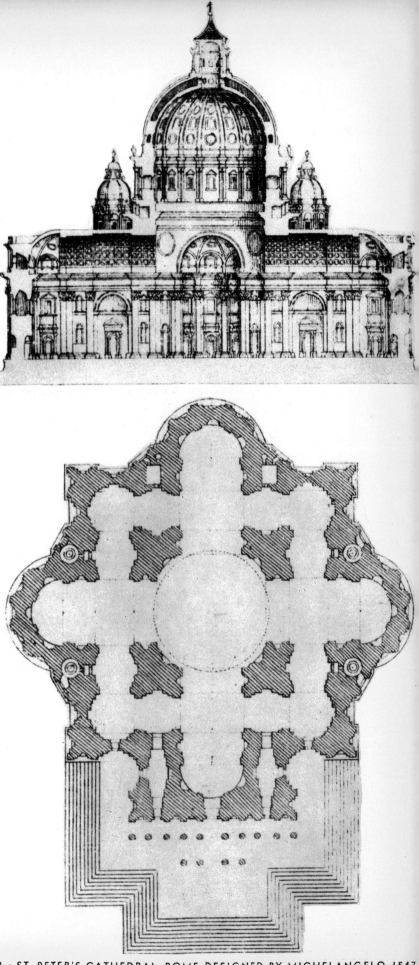

161 · ST. PETER'S CATHEDRAL, ROME DESIGNED BY MICHELANGELO 1547

signed them like large cheap houses.[162] The result was dark, depressing and inefficient.[163] When they put forth a special effort, their contribution consisted primarily of adding something, such as pilasters, and cornices, or other deco-

162 · INTERNATIONAL HARVESTER FACTORY, CHICAGO   DESIGNER UNKNOWN 1899

rations borrowed from antiquity, to mask a structure that should have been approached as a new problem requiring new treatment.

In time, certain American engineers, whose training had been quite different from the architects, began to make progress. These engineers, inspired by economy and mathematics, with the aid of a few sympathetic architects, accepted the machine as the proper inspiration for factory architecture, toward a greater efficiency for the factory itself, toward an honesty and simplification in design. Mr. Henry Ford, being an idealist as well as a practical man, and taking great pride in all phases of his business, in 1924 set a standard with his laboratory.[165] In the exterior, Albert Kahn, the architect, was less successful because he was less straightforward. Here we still see the influence of a past architecture of a different character than the inside of the build-

163 · INTERNATIONAL HARVESTER FACTORY, CHICAGO   DESIGNER UNKNOWN 1899

ing.[164] The cost of this building was several times that of the average factory; consequently it had little effect on factory architecture. Industrial concerns went right on building factories of the eyesore variety both outside and in.[166] Further than this, these average factories have many outstanding faults. There are thousands of feet of exposed trusses which represent an enormous area of dust-collecting surface that is inaccessible, unhealthy and in some instances very detrimental to the work of the machines.[167]

There is a general realization that the basis for success in industry hinges

[203]

on the human factor. In this regard, the relationship existing between employer and employee is of vital importance. This relationship begins with the plant itself. The successful employees are those who have a sincere creative interest in their work, works and workers. Employees are in every sense as susceptible to environment as the employer. The trail for this constructive reasoning was blazed in America and its logic was immediately recognized in Europe. Since then, greater progress in this direction has been seen in the advanced industrial regions of Germany and Holland than in America. Today, however, in America, there is a quickening sense of appreciation on the part of communities regarding the significance of industrial architecture. It promises well for the future.

I digress for a moment to refer to an incident that is interesting because of illustrating how "great oaks from little acorns grow" — how something apparently trivial may lead to something of considerable importance. It concerns a little device that has had its place on my desk for the past twelve years. For years, I had experienced certain inconveniences from working with the standard pen and ink and I had tried all types. I wanted a pen point always full of ink, a holder thick enough to grip firmly, and not lying down

164 · FORD LABORATORY, DEARBORN   DESIGNED BY ALBERT KAHN 1924

Ford Motor Company

but standing ready. I liked thick black India ink, so the fountain pens with their thin inks wouldn't do. India ink required constant recorking or replenishment, owing to evaporation. No great skill was required to carve out a penholder with a barrel that was large enough to hold easily and the right size to serve as a cork in my ink bottle. Dismantling my favorite fountain pen, I attached the pen part to the wooden holder. The finished holder, with its fountain pen point, fitted snugly into the neck of any bottle of India ink and stood there ready for instant use.

Some three years ago, in the course of a conference in my studio, this device came to the attention of Mr. H. D. Bennett, President of the Toledo Scale Company. Previous to this time, I had been commissioned to redesign the products of this company. A business man of the most generous appreciation and penetrating intuitions, the president of the Toledo Scale Company was also vice-president of a leading fountain pen company, and was impressed by the fact that this handy device antedated by several years the more elaborate and refined fountain pen sets now in vogue and in use by millions. A few days later Mr. Bennett telephoned me from Toledo and said he had been unable to get that pen out of his mind and would I be interested in designing a factory.

165 · FORD LABORATORY, DEARBORN   DESIGNED BY ALBERT KAHN 1924

Ford Motor Company

No problem could have more neatly touched my imagination and the query led to fruitful discussion. It was the prelude to one of the most satisfying experiences of my life — an adventure in factory design.

Can a first-rate product be manufactured in a third-rate plant? It is no longer advisable to set up a standardized structure, relying on company engineers to adapt it to company needs.[166] Factory planning presents problems to the architect unlike any other. The architect must be thoroughly familiar with the product to be manufactured and the production methods used. He must *build in* practical solutions of ever-recurring manufacturing problems, such as provision for the elimination of waste materials, the easy shifting of line processes, to say nothing of considering all the factors involved in employees' welfare, lighting, heating, ventilation and cleanliness.

No business man will hear appearance mentioned in connection with factory architecture without raising the question of cost. That question is, indeed, pertinent. What price factory architecture that is pleasing in design? Rather, what price factory architecture with inherent qualities of appeal such that the factory itself may be regarded as of real inspirational value to the workers and of advertising value to the manufacturer by virtue of its effect upon the passerby, who is also the consumer? The answer is that beauty in factory design exacts no premium but can be made to *pay* a premium by diminishing the cost of construction.

No special materials, no costly importations are necessary to this end. What for want of a better term I call beauty in factory architecture must be the result of carefully thought out relationships. It can be achieved by the use of common, standard materials, the cheapest available materials, those that can be most economically assembled and handled. The architect who can plan organically, who can achieve his proportions with the simplest of forms will solve the problem both practically and æsthetically, eliminating factory ugli-

166 · RAYON FACTORYDESIGNED BY J. E. SIRRINE & CO. 1928

ness at *no* premium in cost. Demonstrably, as the architectural effect is achieved, economies occur. It is not too much to say that for *ugliness* in factory architecture the manufacturer pays a premium of from five per cent in excess cost.

How this proposed factory, achieved at no increased cost over the average factory, meets the specific requirements of a plant for the manufacture of a specific product, is the question that I propose to answer. I should like to add that the result was made possible by Mr. Bennett's own point of view and his granting me the fullest freedom in meeting practical as well as æsthetic problems.

167 · GENERAL MOTORS FACTORYDESIGNER UNKNOWN 1929

Motoring from Toledo, Ohio, toward Detroit, on the Dixie Highway, we enter Telegraph Road. The doorway by which all motorists, going in the direction of Detroit, leave Toledo will be a landscape and architectural development for the Toledo Scale Company. Its construction is contemplated at an early date. Down a broad avenue of Lombardy poplars we see the eleven-story administration building of the company's new plant.[168] As planned to-day, the buildings will occupy approximately twenty acres of an eighty-acre tract. The remaining sixty are landscaped, providing space for a private airport and for future expansion of the plant in any direction.

Turning off Telegraph Road and driving up the wide boulevard between two rows of tall trees, we pass around a large reflecting pool which mirrors the tower of the Administration Building.[169] The noticeable feature of this building is the absence of ornamentation and vertical piers which are usual but unnecessary in steel construction. Getting out of our car and approaching the main entrance, we look through a high vaulted arcade and catch the gleam of another pool on the other side.[168] This pool, which is one hundred and twenty feet in diameter, is primarily a fire-protection reservoir. Incidentally, it has been designed for use as a completely equipped swimming tank for employees. The lobby of the administration building is two stories high. In the central section of this building are offices, recreation rooms, lounges and restaurants for the executive departments; the sales school and a display room. The basement provides storage space to meet miscellaneous executive needs.

North of the administration building is the rectangular laboratory building.[169] Since visitors will not be permitted access to the laboratory, there is no "main entrance" at the front, merely the workers' entrance at the rear. The first floor of the laboratory is occupied by the clerical and executive divisions, the second by the chemistry divisions and the third by the engineering division. The basement is a laboratory for testing machines. Flexibility is the outstanding feature of the laboratory. With an area of one hundred and eighty by fifty feet, this space can, by shifting portable partitions, be made

into an open floor or divided into cubicles in multiples of eleven by eleven feet, as required.

A somewhat novel use of an old principle, the so-called cantilever construction, has been used in the laboratory. In consequence, there are no masonry piers in the exterior walls and the maximum of natural illumination is achieved through walls of glass. The building is of such a width that the windows on either side illuminate the full width of the floor.

The mechanical services such as telephones, electricity, water, gas, steam,

Maurice Goldt

170 · TOLEDO SCALE CO.: PRECISION LABORATORY GROUP   DESIGNED BY NORMAN BEL GEDDES 1929

compressed air, waste pipes, exhaust ducts from the various departments are carried up the various columns and between the finished floors and the ceilings directly below them. There are no exposed pipes, beams or other dust-catching surfaces of any nature. Radiators are concealed in the walls under the windows and their heat is introduced into the room through the sloping grilled metal sills. The continuous metal windows are of standard sections with some of the vertical muntins omitted. The ventilating sections are placed in such positions as to give a natural syphon action and also to permit ease of cleaning. Floors are finished with an acid- and alkali-proof mastic material giving a resilient and impervious surface easily cleaned. Toilet and locker rooms are centrally located on each floor and are finished in Carrara glass wainscot and stall partitions with tile floors.

The corners of the building are circular. Wide, overhanging cornices at the corners reduce the glare of cross reflections. Lighting fixtures are provided in the soffits of the cornices for exterior illumination.

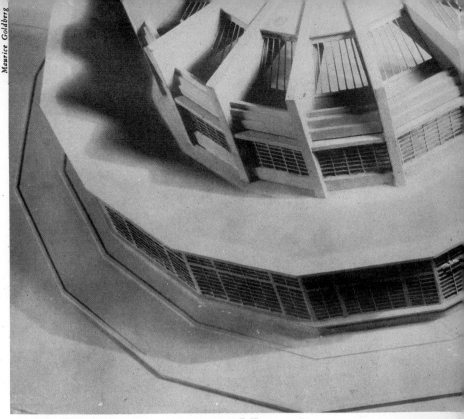

171 · TOLEDO SCALE CO.: MACHINE SHOP
DESIGNED BY NORMAN BEL GEDDES 1929

From the laboratory, by means of a covered corridor, we pass through the receiving and shipping room and enter the machine shop for the manufacture of precision devices. It is a circular building and a marked departure from precedent.[170] It is pertinent to inquire why this particular building was born to be circular. For assembling purposes, a shop of this type requires a certain amount of unobstructed space, with an unusual height of ceiling. Adjacent to this assembling space, manufacturing space with good illumination is required. The high-ceilinged central assembling area is a hundred feet in diameter, unobstructed by columns.[174] Encircling this central area and covered with a circular saw-toothed roof, is a concentric ring of low-ceilinged manufacturing space twenty-two feet in width.[171] This arrangement places the high assembly space adjacent to every part of the manufacturing area.[173]

In this machine shop it was also necessary to provide for future inexpensive

[211]

and rapid expansion. The most economical solution of this particular problem is likewise found in the circular building; for when you increase the radius of a circle twice, you increase the area four times.[173] Provision has been made for the addition of four concentric rings of manufacturing space, each twenty-two feet in width.[170] All of the window units on the lower ring of the circular machine shop are so standardized that when we add additional rings, each of these window or bay units may be moved out and utilized without loss, leaving only the windows in the " saw-tooth " roof which light the area beneath when the additional ring is added.

Manufacturers familiar with the expensive problems of organizing line production requiring operations greatly varied in number will recognize the just claim of the circular factory building to a high-efficiency rating. It permits of any kind of line production, requiring any number of operations. By this method of routing material, varying lengths of process can most easily be provided for with the least possible waste motion. Obviously, the travel around the inner circle is less than that around any outer circle. By radiating aisles, the longer processes easily arrive after traveling the outer circle, in close proximity to the assembling space.

Leaving the machine shop we enter the executives' garage. It is adjacent to the north wing of the administration building and accommodates twenty-five cars with facilities for servicing and washing and attendants' quarters.[169] The walls are of concrete, faced on the inside with glazed tile for ease in cleaning. The main entrance opening on Telegraph Road is sheltered by a semi-circular marquee having a glass soffit above which are placed lights for illuminating the entrance way. Proceeding southwest, across the lawn in front of the administration building, are two hangars and the landing field. These are the private hangars of the Toledo Scale Company.[169] Then we come to the main entrance of the factory building itself.

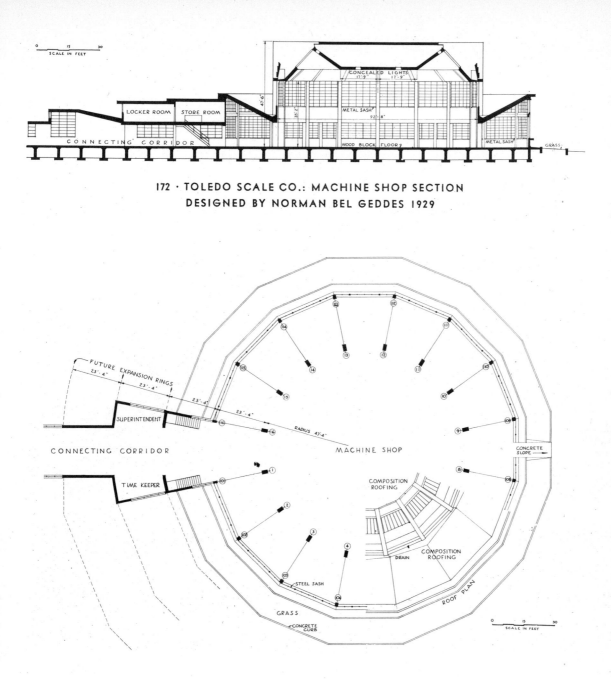

172 · TOLEDO SCALE CO.: MACHINE SHOP SECTION
DESIGNED BY NORMAN BEL GEDDES 1929

173 · TOLEDO SCALE CO.: MACHINE SHOP PLAN
DESIGNED BY NORMAN BEL GEDDES 1929

Approximately six hundred by three hundred and sixty feet, it is a concrete building, without the standard exterior columns of ordinary concrete construction.[175] The layman, I think, would recognize that in exterior appearance this factory has a character that is usually considered appropriate only for a building of better occupancy.[176] He would notice that one continuous window runs around the entire structure and that it is curved at the corners instead of square. The simplest and most significant thing that can be said of the architecture of this building could also be said of the others: it is the direct expression of the purpose for which it is to be used, with no lapse into prettification.

Within, we find one or two genuine innovations in factory construction:

174 · TOLEDO SCALE CO.: MACHINE SHOP   DESIGNED BY NORMAN BEL GEDDES 1929

namely, the degree to which dust-catching surfaces have been eliminated and the method employed for artificial lighting.[177] Here I must express my appreciation to Mr. Bennett for placing due emphasis upon attaining ideal standards for housekeeping in his factory. To eliminate overhead shafting and belts, with the inevitable accompanying dust and dirt,[167] the Toledo Scale Company decided to use machines individually motor driven. Under the entire manufacturing area of this building is a service basement, giving access to the floor from the under side.[177] Through this basement run the ducts and conduits which are ordinarily in an exposed overhead position. All the waste products of manufacturing, such as chips, fumes, and vapor, machine turnings and all blower-system waste are eliminated through the basement. Likewise, all electric, water, steam and telephone services are brought to the various machines through the basement. Provision has been made so that if, eventually, conveyor systems or other material-handling systems are installed, the return of the endless chain will be *under* the manufacturing floor instead of overhead, as in ordinary installations.

The structure is designed so that the roof load is carried by concealed beams.[177] To the under sides of these beams is attached a suspended ceiling covering the entire working area. Heating coils, designed for the columns, are sealed so that only a dust-free circulation of air can ever reach them. Natural day lighting is accomplished by rows of windows placed on the sides of the high bays of the roof which extend the full length of the building. This simple construction permits a maximum of evenly distributed natural light. Sloping window sills, easily wiped free of dust and impossible to use as shelving for miscellaneous articles, have been specified. For the same purpose, round corners are introduced throughout. The common square corner in nearly every factory is a catch-all for a little of everything.

In view of the dust-elimination feature of the design, it is evident that artificial lighting cannot be accomplished by means of suspended fixtures. The lamps are incorporated into continuous V-shaped troughs which project slightly below the white-surfaced ceiling.[177] The troughs with soffits of diffusing lenses are spaced twenty feet on centers and are capable of delivering at the working plane an illumination of twenty-foot candle intensity. This is fully adequate for the most delicate work, the strength of the illumination in a well-lighted living room in the average home being from five to eight-foot candle intensity. These strip lighting fixtures extend the full length of the factory (six hundred feet) and make it impossible for a man at any point in the factory to stand in his own light. With strips as sources of light, rather than points as in the case of suspended fixtures, an overlapping of rays results, and hence the elimination of shadows.

Eyestrain in a factory is due, ordinarily, not so much to a poor quality of light as to glare or an attempt to focus the eye simultaneously on two or more sources of light of widely varying intensities. When two surfaces of varying intensity of light come within the range of vision at one time, the eye cannot

175 · TOLEDO SCALE CO.: FACTORY

adjust itself to both. The lenses in our strip lights diffuse the light over a wide area on the working plane. While diffusing it, they spill enough light onto the ceiling in short rays to eliminate the glare. Important as the elimination of glare in factory surroundings may be, this result was accomplished not as the result of a direct quest for a method of eliminating glare, but as the incidental result of devising new dust-eliminating lighting arrangements.

The working floor surface in this factory is more comfortable than cement, consisting of wood blocks on a sand and tar mat over reinforced concrete slab. In the exterior concrete walls, outside the radiator recesses, insulation is incorporated.

Flexibility, very necessary in factory construction but frequently not achieved, is attained to a marked degree. Instead of attacking the problem from the standpoint of the space the Toledo Scale Company requires at the moment, the entire plot of ground was planned on the estimated basis of what they would require ten years from now. Allowance was made for an area of expansion equal to four times the working space required by their estimated

DESIGNED BY NORMAN BEL GEDDES 1929

development possibilities, and the entire plot was laid out accordingly. Working backward in stages, the areas they need at the present moment were established. The result is that they will expand logically and without running into as many unforeseen complications and problems of space organization as would have happened had the problem been solved on the basis of present requirements.

The factory building is so placed on the lot that it can expand laterally in four directions. Column spacing was determined by the normal distance required for traffic between rows of machines and the most economical structural framing. With the service basement below, it is a simple matter to disconnect the service to any particular machine. The machine can then be moved to another location and reconnected with the necessary services. Since there are no permanent partitions, any department may expand or contract as the need arises. The absence of partitions of any kind makes for better supervision. To double the space of some one department simply means moving the necessary machinery into the adjoining space. Repair of the floor where a machine has stood, where a bolt or connecting member has been carried through, requires only the insertion of a wood block.

Back of this plant is the railroad spur for bringing in coal and bailing out ashes. Trains which bring in raw materials to the factory are completely enclosed. The locomotive does not enter the enclosure. Cars are placed at the shipping platform by an electric mule. At the north end of the factory is a loading dock for motor trucks. Toward the south is the central heating plant with its enormous stack, in approximately the center of the manufacturing area.[168] It conforms to well-established principles of construction and in exterior design follows the main scheme. To the north and west of the factory are parking sheds of fire-proof construction for the accommodation of twenty-five hundred automobiles belonging to employees.

176 · TOLEDO SCALE CO.: FACTORY SIDE ENTRANCE   DESIGNED BY NORMAN BEL GEDDES 1929

The recreation center consists of eight tennis courts, a baseball diamond with a grandstand equipped with showers and locker rooms below, and a wooded picnic ground for the use of employees and their families.[168] The swimming pool previously mentioned is part of the recreation unit. From the pool there is a vista through an avenue cut through the woods. The stream which supplies the swimming pool flows from a mountain source at the end of the avenue through the woods.

Once more passing the swimming pool, we leave the plant through the arcade of the administration building and drive back into Toledo, I hope with the sense of having entered the city by its front door rather than by way of an unsightly backyard which is commonly the feature that distinguishes the approach to our industrial cities.

If the business man inquires at what premium in cost this attempt to eliminate factory ugliness was undertaken, he can be informed that placing buildings in such a manner that they fulfill all their mutual requirements one to the other and form a pleasing appearance adds nothing to the cost; also, that

177 · TOLEDO SCALE CO.: FACTORY   DESIGNED BY NORMAN BEL GEDDES 1929

the materials used throughout are the common standardized products, requiring the less skilled building trades for construction. Owing to the choice of the materials used and the low labor cost to install, the contractor's estimate (1928) on this factory was $2.88 per square foot as against the average factory cost (1928) of $3.00 per square foot.

CHAPTER 11

Product Design as Approached

THE artist's interest in machines has laid the foundation for a new department in industry, in which the relations of product manufacturers and of consumers reach a new level of understanding and congeniality. The artist's contribution touches upon that most important of all phases entering into selling — the psychological. He appeals to the consumer's vanity and plays upon his imagination, and gives him something he does not tire of.

The designer of industrial products can only be successful if he is imbued with the conviction that machines, such as typewriters, automobiles, weighing scales, railway trains, electric fans, radiators, ships, stoves, radios are good to look at when the problems involved are properly solved. An original creative aptitude for materializing this conviction in steel, wood, glass, aluminum, plastic substances and other materials old and new is the *sine qua non* of the profession.

A good illustration of the proper relation between use and appearance is the suspension bridge. A properly designed suspension bridge, regardless of its size, has the utmost simplicity.[178] Its main supporting elements, the cables, hang between their supports as naturally and as gracefully as loose rope. The roadway is suspended from the cables by regularly spaced hangers. The location and direction of the cables and hangers conform to the natural lines of the action of the stresses within them, permitting the most economical use of material in their structional design. There are no superfluous or inefficient members. Inevitably, when all the elements of which the bridge is composed are organically assembled, the structure assumes a pleasing form.

There is an old saying that when a thing is designed right, it looks right. In this connection there arises at once the difficulty that is usually involved in establishing a definition. The terms used may mean entirely different things to different persons. Picasso, for instance, could well make the same statement with regard to one of his compositions;[5] and although Picasso might agree with the work of the engineer,[20] the engineer is not likely to agree with the work of Picasso. An object is well designed when it has been reduced to its utmost simplification in terms of function and form.

While function once arrived at, is fixed, its expression in form may vary endlessly under individual inflection. Form, referring to exterior appearance, always implies a high degree of quality, distinctiveness, and unity with its function. The public generally is unaware that a designer or engineer has enormous latitude in solving a particular problem in the right way. In this respect, engineering, architecture, painting, sculpture, poetry, music and all other media of design resemble one another. This semblance is the starting point of the trouble and it is this that makes the problems interesting. The correct solution of a problem depends on whether the designer is an artist or just a craftsman.

The first scale of the Toledo Scale Company, designed in 1897 by Allen De Vilbiss, functioned satisfactorily.[179] In engineering terms, it was designed right and it looked right. Through years of use and experimentation the

178 · MID-HUDSON BRIDGE: POUGHKEEPSIE   *Ralph Steiner*   DESIGNED BY AMERICAN BRIDGE CO. 1925

original scale was made to function better and also to look better.[180] Its success made it the most popular and most widely used and imitated counter scale on the market. The problem of improving the design of this scale was given to me. My recommendations were slight and yet somewhat radical. There are two outstanding faults in the design of the existing scale, — one its weight, since it is made almost entirely of cast iron, and the other its large bulk. I redesigned the body to be made out of thin pressed metal, recommending aluminum. So that the purchaser may see simultaneously what is being weighed and its correct weight, the pendulum mechanism is located at one side and the cylinder mechanism cantilevered.[181] The form of the enclosing body is simplified as much as possible and the only further recommendation I made was to set the scale into the counter, so that the weighing platform would be flush with the wrapping surface.

Mr. Bennett had an idea for a new type of scale which he called the Island Scale.[182] This is a mobile unit combining the weighing scale with weighing platform set flush with the wrapping counter, and facilities for holding rolls of paper, string, tape, and paper bags. This unit can be moved to any position in the store, where there is no counter, or even out on to the sidewalk where the fresh vegetables might be displayed. The unit is a good illustration of an executive applying creative thought to his own products. Not alone in new problems, but in old products to be brought up to date it is essential to discard traditions and ideas of a hampering kind and take advantage of new ideas, new materials and new methods of production.

Much might be said of the necessary routine procedure in the creation of a new design before the designer so much as attempts a sketch. For the sake of concreteness, I will describe the routine that is observed in my own office.

When a new problem comes up for design, all my associates, those who will be connected with the problem in any responsible way, gather in my office and discuss the problem in all its phases. Depending upon the nature of the subject, different types of designers, engineers, merchandisers and research specialists are present. To insure clarity of purpose and thoroughness, we proceed in accordance with a check list which has become more and more standardized with each new job. We determine the specific objectives and lay out the various means of achieving those objectives. A working schedule is laid out in weekly units. Later on, a detailed, day-to-day schedule covering all details of the work is made. These schedules are agreed to whole-heartedly by every one in any way connected with them, and each person assumes responsibility for his or her part of the schedule. The discipline of maintaining a prearranged plan, schedule and set of restrictions is of great value. Continual analysis imposes integrity and directness in the mental processes and eliminates guessing and whimsies.

Our ground work is founded wholly on facts. All records in my office are kept in writing. Verbal understandings do not count. All decisions arrived at in every meeting of consequence among ourselves or between clients and ourselves are covered by a stenographic record in the form of minutes. A copy of the minutes is sent to every one present at the meeting, within twenty-four hours after the meeting, for approval or correction. This practice prevents misunderstandings and in several instances has prevented losses of thousands of dollars.

Design problems vary not only with each industry and with each product, but with each manufacturer. The first step after determining the specific objective is to become familiar with the object to be designed: the thing it does or should do, the way it is made, sold, serviced; its good qualities and its unsatisfactory features. In short, all possible information must be gathered about every matter that can in any way influence the design. Specifically, these are recognized as the fundamental preliminaries to the actual creation of a design: The client's factory is visited, to study the methods and equipment for the production of the product in its present form. This visit is imperative if the designer is to produce designs that can be executed with existing facilities. Also, at this time, the designer gets from the client cost details which enable him to keep the new design within a certain price range, and all other available information concerning the product. Simultaneously, the designer consults recognized authorities on materials, construction, production and finish. He acquaints himself with the methods of merchandising and servicing used by not only the client but his competitors. He searches past and present books, periodicals and reports from various firms, associations and libraries. He makes a comparative study of the lines of outstanding competitors. As occasion requires, he conducts a survey among users of the existing product, seeking comment, criticism and suggestions; and, in addition, a survey of dealers for the same data. The client or his advertising agency has usually made a survey that can supply much valuable data. Nevertheless the designer's point of view is sufficiently different to find little of concrete value in surveys made by others. This research and study is done entirely from the standpoint of *design*.

The experience of my own organization convinces me that the survey to acquire impressions and interpretation of users is of considerable value in certain instances. Approaching problems involved in the design of weighing scales, radios, gas stoves, I assigned various individuals with proper qualifications to go into carefully selected parts of the country to make numerous specific inquiries. Among these investigators were designers, merchandising specialists, salesmen, engineers; men to get the men's point of view, women to get the reaction of women. The various areas covered were selected for one specific reason or another. They represented every phase of normal contemporary living conditions, varying from the metropolis to the scantily

Toledo Scale Company

179 · TOLEDO COUNTER SCALE   DESIGNED BY ALLEN DeVILBISS 1897

populated rural commu-
nity.

For this type of work I used very few professional canvassers. Experiment has convinced me that they fail to get the best results. It is my practice to send out personable men and women who are not in a hurry, who can be depended upon to cover the ground and sub-ject thoroughly. These investigators call on individuals in their homes, where they sit and chat for perhaps fifteen minutes. Sometimes two or three of the neighbors are invited to participate. It may prove to be an animated session and of real value for our purpose. Always, these investigators have a dozen fundamental questions for each person to answer. We have found that no topic is as easy to use as an opening wedge for door-to-door conversation as how to improve the attractiveness of the home. Questions are not asked directly and answers are not written down in the presence of the person inter-rogated. The written report is made out immediately after the termination of the interview. All reports are mailed in daily. This data is sorted and compiled in statistical form as it arrives at the office.

As an indication of the type of information these surveys produce, I list a few questions from past solicitations regarding radios: Is there anything you do not like about your radio: Tone quality? Clarity of reception? Style or design of cabinet? Size? Hard to dust? Operating cost? Maintenance cost? Would you prefer to have your radio concealed in a piece of furniture such as: Table? Desk? Bookcase? Chest? Clock? Drawers? Would you prefer a radio that could be installed in a closet, basement or other concealed location, providing it functioned just as well? Would you prefer your radio cabinet to have: Legs with stretchers? Legs without stretchers? No legs? Would you like your radio cabinet to have doors? What type of covering would you prefer over the speaker? Would you like incorporated in your radio: Clock? Reading lamp? Ash tray? Other feature?

Here are a few questions from past solicitations regarding gas stoves: What finish would you like if you were buying a new stove: Enamel? Lacquer? Natural metal such as stainless steel? What criticism have you of your present stove: Heats kitchen excessively? Hard to clean? Finish unsatisfactory? How? Broiler unsatisfactory? How? Oven not large enough? Would you prefer the cooking surface of your stove to be: Solid? Grilled? Why? Would you like to have your stove combined with other kitchen furniture: Cabinet? Refrigerator? What color combinations do you prefer? Solid Colors — Black? White? Natural metal such as stainless steel? Other colors? What special features would you like built into your stove: Clock? Heat control? Time control? Insula-

180 · TOLEDO COUNTER SCALE   DESIGNED BY TOLEDO SCALE CO. 1925

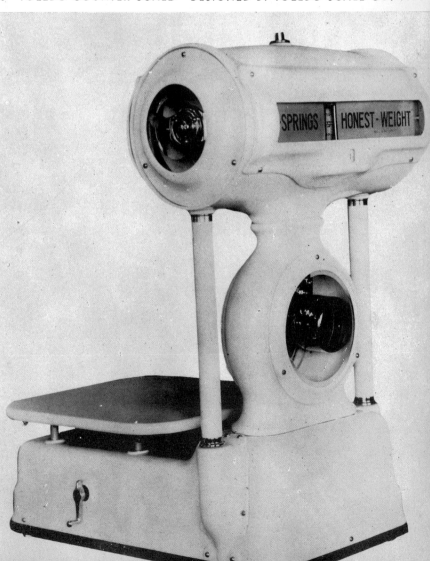

tion? Electric toaster? Electric percolator? Electric waffle iron? Automatic instant lighter? Safety valve?

One of the most valuable places for getting information of this general character is aboard different classes of railway trains. If the research person is a good conversationalist with pleasing personality, has consideration for others, together with something resembling a sense of humor, he or she can accomplish a good deal in a short space of time. It is a simple matter to turn a dining or club-car conversation from one subject to another. The important factor in conducting a survey of this kind is to pick the right individuals from whom to get information. The survey should represent the average mass viewpoint, the viewpoint of the greatest buying power.

181 · TOLEDO COUNTER SCALE
DESIGNED BY NORMAN BEL GEDDES 1929

As an instance of the value of information attained by the survey method, I may cite one example. When I undertook the design of radios for one of the large companies in this field, I asked a member of the client's engineering department what the public's preference was regarding stretchers. As you probably know, a stretcher is the horizontal member of the frame near the floor that connects the legs of cabinet or table to give it greater rigidity. The answer to my question was that it made no difference from any standpoint other than the strength of the cabinet. In our radio survey this same question was asked of hundreds and hundreds of users. The result showed that sixty-four per cent of the persons interviewed objected to stretchers because they made cleaning under the cabinet difficult.

Once having acquired all the information he can about the product, and having established clearly in his own mind and that of his client what purposes and conditions the product must meet, *then* the designer applies himself to the problem of redesign. The first step in this work is one of organizing it. For this, I use a card-index system, consisting of several hundred printed forms-covering every phase of every type of work, a system that makes it utterly impossible to overlook any development or phase of any type of problem. I am in no hurry to start preliminary sketches[201] until these ideas are clearly visualized in my

mind and the minds of my assistants. A drawing involves comparatively little work on the part of a draftsman after he once has his facts and objective clearly in mind. There is no use putting hand to paper until you can close your eyes and see with *complete* clarity all details of what it is you wish to draw.

One great misconception is prevalent regarding design. Design is not pri-

marily a matter of drawing but a matter of *thinking*. Personally, I do comparatively little drawing. The bulk of this is in the nature of preliminary sketches[201] and in criticising designs in course of development. This is a matter of daily procedure. Every drawing, at every stage of the work, from the preliminary sketches up to the final shop drawings, passes across my desk for approval or criticism before it advances to the next stage. While drawings are being worked on, I go over them daily in the drafting room.

After a design has been approved by the client in finished sketch form,[202] it is developed into the working drawing stage.[203-204] By this I mean that it is restudied at larger scale which requires greater accuracy and a thorough consideration of details. Full-sized models are then made of wood or metal, depending on circumstances.[196-197] They are completely finished, so that the client can get an accurate impression of the appearance of his product in its final form.

The aims and approach of the industrial designer may appear in a more revealing light if we consider them from a somewhat different angle. For purposes of illustration, suppose we discuss the various problems suggested by metal furniture. Wood for a long time has been looked on as the natural

183 · BRASS BED   DESIGNER UNKNOWN 1890

material for furniture. Tradition and custom favor it, so much so that, until recently, manufacturers of metal furniture could not hope to compete for popular preference with the manufacturer of wood furniture.[185] But metal is now a promising and pro-

Brown Brothers

gressive rival, and its use in making furniture, is, I believe, destined presently to be far more extensive than now. In the home of the future, metal furniture will neither be odd nor distasteful, but a commonplace.

Any competent designer who, after working in wood, turns to the problems involved in the creation of metal furniture, must inevitably be refreshed and stimulated by the infinitely interesting variety of new forms that suggest themselves. He sees some old conventions vanish, finds new liberties permitted and likewise new restrictions imposed. He confronts an inviting problem in craftsmanship — the use of machines to stamp out of metal a product that shall be æsthetically expressive, graceful, comfortable, and at the same time characteristic of the material used. In addition, he has to solve new problems with regard to surface and finish. The adaptability of corrugated steel and steel tubing is in itself a fascination.

Metal furniture that does not seek to meet the problem sincerely is by no means new. Made to look like wood, with telltale imitation finish in oak or mahogany, it has long been made after designs originally conceived for wooden furniture.[184] But if the metal is treated as metal, exploiting rather than concealing the nature of the material, then not only is the taint of a fake avoided but the problem is approached in a manner that allows it to capitalize on its own values and make possible an interesting solution. Imagine an armchair made of steel tubing modeled and painted as a convincing imitation of a wooden Colonial chair. Sit in it, touch it. The sound and touch of the deception remind you that you are duped by a pretentious substitute. Imagine another chair, also of steel tubing. There is nothing wrong with tubing. It provides flexibility, a pleasant springy ease. Lacquered or chromium-plated and finished with an upholstered seat, it is a practical chair, adaptable to many informal uses. It is obviously metal but neither substitute nor fake, and it solves in its own honest way the problem as to what kind of chair this chair

[233]

should be, and defies imitation in wood. It can be fabricated and sold at considerably less than the imitation Windsor chair.

The designer who has in hand the problem of a metal bed, for instance, is well advised if he does not ponder too long the beds of history and still less contemporary beds. His object should be to analyze the bed in its fundamental terms. The main elements of a bed are the mattress and spring. The construction is nothing more than something to hold the mattress and springs.[185] As for headboard, footboard, legs; they are matters of individual taste.[186] The bed should be off the floor, not only to give the mattress more spring, which means comfort, but to let air circulate under it and to facilitate keeping the space under it clean.

In connection with metal furniture as with other products, the problems of color and finish open a large field to the designer. Lacquer, which is at present the usual finish for steel furniture, can be obtained in a large range of colors. In the last few years, the colors themselves have been greatly improved. Muddy and chalky colors have been replaced by good clear colors. An ever increasing range of trims is being perfected. Chromium, aluminum and brass are among the more obvious. In general, the designer is faced by three major considerations in specifying color for his product: color that is appropriate to the product itself, color that is appropriate to the environment and ultimate setting of the product, and color that will arouse a buying interest in the prospective customer.

Aside from color, there are at least two cardinal principles by which the designer should always be guided: simplicity and the use of interesting materials. Simplicity means, of course, the avoidance of excess decoration and the elimination of every unnecessary detail. The designer who works in industrial fields is using, instead of pigment on canvas, or marble, a combination of materials that are the development of this age. They are as different from the materials of the painter as the materials of the painter are from the materials of the sculptor. In addition, of course, he has æsthetic problems to solve — proportion, for instance. There is a great difference between merely satisfying proportion and the proportioning of a form that gives it added interest, vitality, conviction and distinction.

Whether the utility of the product involves one unit or the combination of a number of units, the same reasoning is applied to each. If it involves more than one unit, the designer first applies his principles to the group in terms of function, organism, and proportion, reducing the several required masses to one mass, placing all the forms in their proper sequence and combination. He brings the component parts into a unified whole, with no unnecessary embellishments or foibles.

A radio receiving set for the home consists of three major groups of parts:

184 · SIMMONS STEEL BED

DESIGNED BY C. A. STUART 1927

Simmons Company

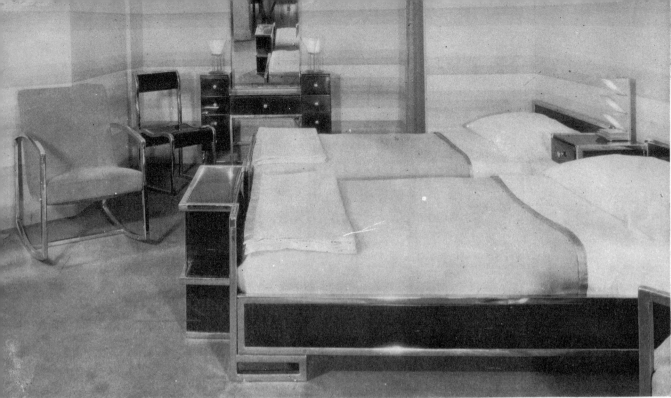

 is shown with the following attribution in the right margin:

Creative Studios, Inc.

the receiving and amplifying mechanism, called the chassis; the speaker, and the baffle. In early radios there was no baffle and no attempt was made to organize the chassis mechanism and the speaker into a piece of furniture.[187]

The chassis is the assembly of tubes, condensers and other electrical apparatus arranged on a base and connected in such a manner as to receive, select and amplify the radio waves to an intensity that will actuate the speaker magnet. The speaker is a diaphragm of lightweight material, usually conical in shape, vibrating with the fluctuations of current delivered to an electromagnet from the receiver. It operates in much the same manner as a telephone receiver. The baffle is a plate of any material to which the speaker is attached. Its function is to separate the sound waves that emanate from the front of the speaker from those that emanate from the back, so that they reach the auditor's ear without interference which causes imperfect reception. The effect of the baffle is to bring out the low bass and high treble notes in proper relation to the intermediate notes, giving a full, rounded tone. Without the baffle, the speaker gives a hollow, harsh tone. Experiments show that the ideal baffle to date is of wood having a period of vibration below that of the lowest bass notes, so that no audible sympathetic vibrations are created and of such dimensions that the sound travels at least a distance of about four feet from the front to the back of the speaker cone. A wooden disc forty-eight inches in diameter meets these requirements.

There is no fixed size for the chassis or for the speaker, as they vary with the type of set, its capacity, and arrangement of elements. Any combination of the above variables will again vary with the manufacturer. Only wire connection is necessary between the chassis mechanism and the cone. In other words, the chassis can be in another part of the house or elsewhere, provided there are additional wires for remote control, since its location depends only

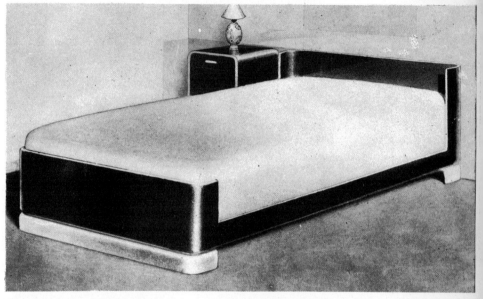

186 · SIMMONS STEEL BED   DESIGNED BY NORMAN BEL GEDDES 1929

on the accessibility of the controls for changing station and volume. The cone, with the baffle board, can stand free or it may be assembled with the chassis in one unit. The cone would work as satisfactorily if the baffle were set flush into a ceiling or wall, and there is no reason why the cone should be any less attractive in design than any object in the room. For that matter, the cone can be built, as is the common practice, in a cabinet.

I have been speaking in terms of a Class A radio. For smaller and cheaper sets, the same conditions govern. Obviously, in cheaper sets, with chassis containing fewer tubes and a smaller-sized cone with a reduced baffle, the quality is not so good, but that is the only essential difference.

There is no doubt in my mind that radio cabinets will soon be manufactured of a composition material instead of wood. When the cost of molded plastics comes into the competitive price range of other less satisfactory materials and under the price of wood, there is no doubt that they will be used far more extensively than now for radios. The best-looking radio I have ever seen was an experimental one which consisted of nothing but the essential knobs, switches, and indicating devices mounted on a black bakelite panel without frills or ornament. Bakelite has been used for many years in electrical laboratories for panel boards, instrument boards and the like, but its cost of manufacture except in large quantities is high.

Keystone View

187 · RADIO   DESIGNED BY FREED-EISEMAN 1924

So far, plastic materials in other than flat sheets have only been extensively used for small items such as powder containers, cigarette boxes, knobs. Methods of fabrication are such that the initial investment in equipment is very great and the materials have not been sufficiently developed to warrant larger articles.

The material and the manufacturing process of plastics make it possible to get every variety of molded form with great detail and sharpness. Bakelite, Plaskon, Lumarith and Beetleware are all essentially synthetic resins, the chemical compositions of which are generally kept secret. However, the variations between the various formulæ are not great and the technique of manufacture is essentially the same. So far as appearance is concerned, there is only a slight difference. Some of these materials are more adaptable to light colors than others. Plaskon has a very complete color range without the chalky appearance of other resins.

Limitations in the use of these materials will presently be overcome. It will be practicable to use molds of larger size. A decrease in the time required for the materials to set will make them available for large cabinets at a much lower cost than at present for wood. An all-metal radio with its appearance depending on exquisite proportions rather than embellishments, should be interesting, attractive, and easy to manufacture.

The ultimate solution of the radio problem will undoubtedly be met by permanent installation. However, this solution will hardly be practicable until radios are improved to the point where they may be relied upon as we rely upon electric light or plumbing. While we may anticipate that remote control will be in general use ultimately, it still is comparatively expensive.

188 · VICTOR PHONOGRAPH
DESIGNER UNKNOWN 1911

The present radio cabinet has had a similar history to the automobile, in that it grew out of something else. The first company of any size to manufacture quality radios was one that had manufactured phonographs for many years. The phonograph was an outgrowth of the music cabinet.[188] The bulk of the cabinet was used for the storage of records. Approximately one eighth of it was required for the mechanism. In order to get the record platform up to a convenient height for a person to operate while standing, the cabinet was built high. The Victor Company had successfully made Victrola cabinets for many years. After being forced to enter the radio field, it was absorbed by the Radio Corporation of America, which utilized in the making of radios the facilities formerly used in making Victrola cabinets. As a result, there was little difference in appearance between a radio and a Victrola. Moreover, the better machines were combinations of radio and phonograph. Other radio companies followed the lead of the Victor people. Though this practice is no longer common, radio cabinets still are designed and built in the same general form. Radios are still in their horseless carriage days.

But the basic form is not the worst feature of the present radio cabinet. It is the lack of taste in proportion and detail. With reason, one might hold that a

189 · PHILCO RADIO   DESIGNED BY PHILCO ENGINEERING DEPT. 1930

radio cabinet should be designed as of a definite period, that is, Tudor, or Louis XIV, or Jacobean. It is hardly reasonable, however, to assume that a respectable piece of furniture can be a combination of all three. On the other hand, it might be assumed that a radio need reflect none of these periods, but have a form that would be appropriate anywhere, due to its simplicity and dignity.[190] Instead of accepting this point of view, some manufacturers reason that if a radio were designed as simply as a grand piano, for instance, it would not appeal to popular taste. Hence, a style of a purely mongrel nature which few persons of taste can tolerate.[189] There is a still stranger point of view in the industry at the moment — to disguise the fact that a radio is a radio.

Many manufacturers are designing clocks and putting radio chassis and speaker inside them. They are doing the same thing with desks and tables. It is contrary to all principles of good design to represent an object on the outside as something other than it really is. Essentially the radio is one of the most representative products of the modern era, an era in which the mechanistic and the æsthetic are related. Its future design will proceed upon this basis.

190 · PHILCO RADIO   DESIGNED BY NORMAN BEL GEDDES 1931

Maurice Goldberg

CHAPTER 12

Unexplored Fields for the Designer

T HERE are, in the main, five reasons why far-sighted manufacturers are eager to incorporate good design in their products:

Good design offers new advertising opportunities. Good design increases sales appeal in any object. Good design instills a pride of ownership which increases the value of the piece. It creates favorable discussion by word-of-mouth advertising (the most valuable kind) that is totally lacking in an object of mediocre design. Good design adds length of life to an object because it takes longer to tire of it. Good design tends towards further simplification of manufacturing processes and hence to economies in production. Good design improves the merit of the product.

There are many fields offering great opportunities to the merchant and designer that are as yet untouched. Consider the chain stores, for instance. Their appeal is to the woman of moderate means and they should be dressed accordingly. No one will deny that in any community where two or more chain stores engage in competition, the store with the more inviting front and interior (factors of merchandise, prices, and service being equal) has the greater success. Nevertheless, chain stores are fundamentally lacking in appeal. The same is true of some of our largest department stores. Their interiors, display systems, show cases, specialty shops, are more valuable in psychological selling terms than the daily newspaper space they pay so much for.

Consider other subjects than stores. You have only to visualize present-day electric street cars and interurban cars to realize how old-fashioned they are in every particular. In this field much experimental work is under way. Mechanical improvements are being studied by competent engineers. But engineers are only farseeing in terms of engineering. The engineering problems are the most obvious and easiest division of the problem to solve. The one important factor that would get people into the cars is being almost completely ignored. Competition between the various transportation systems will undoubtedly bring about a change for the better before long.

Outdoor fields, rich in design possibilities which have scarcely been touched, are too numerous to mention. Offhand, I think of the following, — bus terminals, gas and oil service stations, amusement parks, race tracks, bathing beaches, hotels, and advertising piers such as those at Atlantic City. Even so, I have not included the two fields that have been most conspicuously neglected, — business offices in general, including conference,[191] executive, sales offices, and the home.

Go into the office of the general manager of any business. Examine his desk. Does it *look* especially businesslike? If it does, I venture to say it is because he keeps it cleared of papers. Look at the objects on his desk, starting, if you like, with the telephone. Consider the telephone as though you had never seen one before. Every time the telephone company redesigns the instrument they improve on it measurably. Few people are aware of the innumerable parts of which it is composed. Its problems of design are many. The latest type of desk set is still clumsy. It is certainly not an object of

191 · CONFERENCE ROOM: J. WALTER THOMPSON CO.

Mary Dale Clarke

DESIGNED BY NORMAN BEL GEDDES 19

beauty. In an office this is less important but there are millions of telephones in homes. I predict that five years hence this object which we now accept as it is, will have been replaced by one much better looking.

Similar observations apply to the office inkwell and to all the fancy marbilized fountain pen sets now in vogue. The principle of these sets is thoroughly sound, but, translated into terms of visual design, it has lost all individuality. Is there any reason why a fountain pen, or the fixture that holds it, should be made to look like marble? Why not paint the top of your desk the same way? Another object on the desk that needs redesigning from every standpoint is the calendar pad. I have yet to see a business calendar pad of modest size so laid out that it is useful in the way it should be. It does not even serve the purpose of appointments to the extent it should. A few larger sizes do, but they are cumbersome and take up too much room. Lamps, clocks, receptacles for cigarettes, cigars and pipe tobacco, all are mediocre-looking objects of the business man.

Adding machines, calculating machines, time clocks, filing cabinets are examples of business equipment whose appearance has never been considered of importance from their visual viewpoint. The same is true of more specialized office equipment. The dictating machine is an example. I am a confirmed dictaphonist and I have used the machines for years, in my office, in my bedroom, and when I travel. Nevertheless, I hide my dictating machine. Don't misunderstand me. I am not ashamed of it. I do not object because it is a piece of machinery. A machine is no disgrace in my office, but it is not a properly designed machine to go on or in a desk. The base, holding the major part of the mechanism, occupies too much room on a desk or directly adjacent to it. Moreover, it is a great dust-catching invention, and the wax dust from the cylinder has a way of floating about. These are defects in design that could easily be remedied, and, if overcome convincingly, old confirmed users would be on the prospect list for new and better machines.

The elimination of dust-catching surfaces is one of the most important considerations for the designer of office equipment. In this connection the typewriter is a good example. Although the settling of dust upon the keys and other delicate features of the mechanism does not materially affect its operation, dust gives the mechanism an unsightly aspect and one that any neat office worker resents. Cleaning a typewriter thoroughly requires time. Time in any office costs some one money. If it is not cleaned every day or two, the dirt becomes conspicuous. Despite the fact that this could be easily overcome, nothing has been done about it. One or two attempts have been made to improve the appearance of the typewriter, but with negligible results, and the efforts in this direction seem to have been abandoned. In this connection the president of one of the leading office appliance companies in the United States told me an amusing story.

This manufacturer decided to have his machine redesigned. It is one of the oldest and most popular office appliances in the country. After the expenditure of considerable money and time, the new machine was ready to put on the market. The publicity department discovered that the man who sold the first machine of this particular make, many years before, was still about. They decided to have a photograph taken of him with the previous model and the new model. This was arranged. The salesman was placed behind a table with the old and new models on each side of him. When the photographs were available, they were shown around the advertising department, and the first remark that any

192 · STOOL: J. WALTER THOMPSON COMPANY
DESIGNED BY NORMAN BEL GEDDES 1928

Maurice Goldberg

one was heard to make was "Which is the new model?"

This story illustrates two things. First, how an executive who is very close to his product has difficulty in looking at the problem through any eyes other than those of a fond parent; and may have looked with timidity on the recommendations of the surgeon-designer he called in to diagnose and operate. Second, how a designer, lacking convictions or courage, or both, must fail to achieve the result that the manufacturer has a right to expect. In this case the designer had either not shown enough initiative or enough force or the executive had mistaken minor improvements for major improvements. The difference between the old and new models was so slight that the public could not be expected to react enthusiastically and so the job is still to be done.

It is the designer's fresh viewpoint, his viewpoint as an outsider in conjunction with his viewpoint as a specialist in the appearance of things, that gives him his great advantage. A survey of the mechanical equipment of the modern home leads to the same conclusion as a survey of the business office. There is a field of great commercial promise for a good-looking portable bookcase. Hundreds of thousands of

193 · STAIRS: J. WALTER THOMPSON COMPANY
DESIGNED BY NORMAN BEL GEDDES 1928

dollars are spent annually by tenants who build permanent bookcases in apartments where these bookcases must be left when the tenants move. The radiator in terms of being attractive, both of the free standing and built-in wall type, is being given considerable thought lately, but in terms of results is an untouched field. Think of lighting and plumbing fixtures! In terms of design they are psychologically still in the Victorian era. The same is true with the majority of most hardware equipment, such as door knobs and hinges. Window sash has taken tremendous strides but their hardware is poor. In crockery and utensils of heat-proof glass, above all, in appliances such as carpet sweepers, dish washers, ironers, electric irons, sewing machines, vacuum cleaners, washing machines, sinks and kitchen cabinets, a radical improvement in design is bound to show itself before long. There is on the market a single kitchen unit which includes stove, sink, refrigerator, incinerator and cabinet, but it represents a premature version of a problem that will require a great amount of design study.

At Schenectady, the General Electric Company has a laboratory working on future engineering developments. The plan and scope of this work will eventually alter profoundly the trend of our lives generally. This laboratory, its research and experimentation, is the heart of the General Electric Company. Without it the business would settle and ossify. With it there is no limiting its horizon. The same can be said of the General Motors Laboratory and of others. Laboratories make a daily habit of peering over the horizon. The laboratory in any industry, and what the laboratory produces, represents the future development of that business. The forward-seeing designer offers a parallel contribution in this development work that, up to the present, has appeared as an afterthought. Several of the most interesting problems we are working on in my office are of a laboratory nature and cannot be described here, because they must be treated as confidential until released to the buying public. A discussion of one interesting problem and its solution may throw light upon the results that may be expected when the designer, with the full coöperation of his client, enters a field that he has had no experience in and one that has hitherto been practically unexplored from the standpoint of visual design. My subject is a gas stove for the Standard Gas Equipment Corporation.

It should be clearly understood that the utility and conditions of design, production, distribution, and merchandising, determine the design of a gas stove as of any other object. Not only must these conditions be met by the designer but he must meet them in a manner that improves the appearance of the product and without increasing the cost of manufacture. How these problems were solved in this instance can best be understood in the light of conditions faced at the start.

194 · VULCAN GAS RANGE   DESIGNED BY W. M. CRANE CO. 1911

In the early days of the gas stove, the precedent of wood and coal stoves prevailed, the problem being treated as one merely of adaptation.[194] No particular thought was given to sanitation or to ease of cleaning. The body was of sheet iron with cast iron trimmings, the cocks and manifold of wrought iron. The finish was stove blacking applied to the sheet iron. In the kitchen, the

Standard Gas Equipment Corp.

stove was a hideous thing, unsatisfactory in arrangement and operation, with inaccessible corners and pockets, covered with smoke and grease.

When I undertook to design stoves, only one or two manufacturers had discarded the custom of constructing the gas range, in part at least, of cast iron. This was the result of precedent and the fact that manufacturers had equipment for making cast iron. Old stove lines were, of course, adhered to. One of the great drawbacks of the practice in favor was that pressed steel and cast iron in combination necessitated certain joints, certain lines of design, and certain other practices which worked against both economy and appearance.

A couple of years ago the American Stove Company introduced a new line of gas ranges which they named The Magic Chef.[195] In this line they introduced a comparatively simplified type of design which immediately caught the eye of the public and within a short time led the market in sales. On looking at this stove, the question immediately asked is: should a stove fit, in appearance, with the refrigerator, cabinets, sinks, and the other dominant kitchen features, as harmoniously as possible? Most of these units are white or ivory in finish. White is universally accepted as the most sanitary color. Other colors are more restful to the eye than white, but isn't white the safest practice until manufacturers adopt a joint policy regarding colors and finishes?

The stoves of practically every manufacturer, including those of my client, contained shelves and interior corners which only the most diligent housekeeper could keep clean. Generally these places collected greases and other deposits from cooking, which eventually caked and spread, until the range was anything but attractive in appearance. In the stove of my client, the open, cook-top construction exposed the greater part of the burner castings to spillage of liquids from utensils on the grates above the burners. To clean these parts required the removal of the top grates. Drip pans underneath were intended to catch spillage, and did so, but *after* deposits had been left on the exposed parts.

Consider what has been accomplished by this new design for the benefit of the consumer. The first impression is one of the utmost simplicity.[196] The stove has no projections or dirt-catching corners, the fewest possible cracks or joints where dirt can accumulate. Burner castings formerly exposed to spillage are protected by an aëration plate which is as easily cleaned as a china bowl.

In color, the stove is ivory-white enamel with the hardware in chromium plating. It has a china-like surface of vitreous enamel which shines when it is clean, and it is easily kept

American Stove Company

195 · MAGIC CHEF GAS STOVE
DESIGNED BY N. Y. SCHOOL OF FINE & APPLIED ART 1929

clean. Immaculateness was a major consideration in the design. A housewife would be surprised to see no evidence whatever that this enameled cabinet is a stove. Even the heat control is concealed by a lift cover.[197] The doors are flush with the front.

The cooking part of the range is assembled, one unit above the other, into one tier. This arrangement permits convenient transfer of foods from the top of the stove to the oven or vice versa. The oven door opens out to a horizontal position, forming a convenient shelf on which a roast can rest while being inspected.[198] The oven shelves lock so that they cannot

196 · S.G.E. GAS STOVE   DESIGNED BY NORMAN BEL GEDDES 1932

be accidentally pulled all the way out.

The utility space is on the left side of the stove.[196] A shallow drawer for knives, spoons and flat utensils is at the level of the cook-top. Directly beneath is a utility cabinet in which may be stored large cooking utensils. Beneath this is another and larger drawer for pot lids and similar utensils. This drawer is on rollers for ease and quietness in operation. The handles of all the drawers are designed as simply as possible.

197 · S. G. E. GAS STOVE: COOK TOP
DESIGNED BY NORMAN BEL GEDDES 1932

They are easy to take hold of, insulated so as never to be hot, and finished in chromium.

In the manner of the modern built-to-the-floor bathtub, the stove has no legs. This eliminates the necessity of cleaning beneath it. The solid base, finished with black enamel, recedes. To some extent this permits getting closer to the cooking surface. If anything is inadvertently spilled on the front of the range and runs down the base, it drops to the linoleum and can be easily removed.

Now let us consider what the design has accomplished from the manufacturing viewpoint. When work was started on this problem, we discovered that the client was making approximately one hundred different models composed of several hundred different units such as broilers and ovens. One of our aims was to standardize the different parts so that, without alteration, the same part,

198 · S. G. E. GAS STOVE: BROILER & OVEN
DESIGNED BY NORMAN BEL GEDDES 1932

Maurice Goldberg

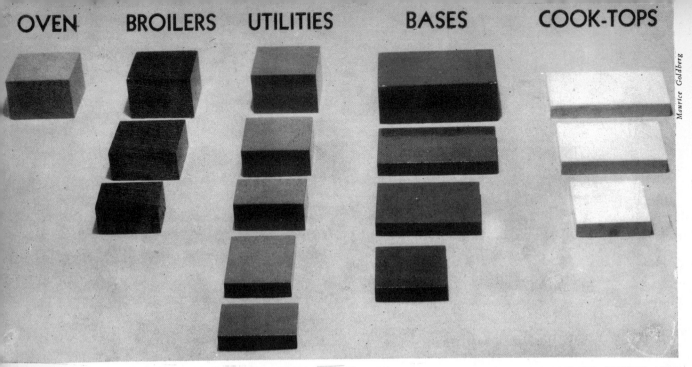

Maurice Goldberg

199 · BLOCKS REPRESENTING DIFFERENT SIZES OF STOVE UNITS.   DESIGNED BY NORMAN BEL GEDDES 1931.

the oven for instance, could be used in all models. Thus, the necessity of making a dozen different sized ovens is eliminated. The same procedure was followed with regard to other parts. A series of blocks were made, painted different colors to represent different classes of units,[199] and the various combinations[200] checked with the client. Eventually, after determining proper sizes, it was found that the equivalent of most of the hundred stoves that the client was then making could be made in four models, using only twelve different standardized units in various combinations.[202]

As already indicated, gas ranges have been, until now, primarily a combination of sheet and cast iron. For many reasons this is objectionable. Consequently I evolved a method of construction that eliminates cast iron completely. These two results, standardization and sheet-metal construction

200 · THREE COMBINATIONS OF BLOCK UNITS   DESIGNED BY NORMAN BEL GEDDES 1931.

Maurice Goldberg

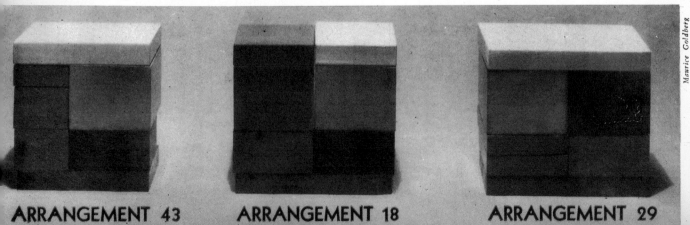

ARRANGEMENT 43   ARRANGEMENT 18   ARRANGEMENT 29

throughout, are illustrative of what may follow from the application of a fresh point of view to a manufacturer's problem.

In the design of this stove one of the important items that had to be considered was the extensive loss sustained by the manufacturer, due to the fragile characteristics of enamel. The greater proportion of these enamel losses occurred when the assembler

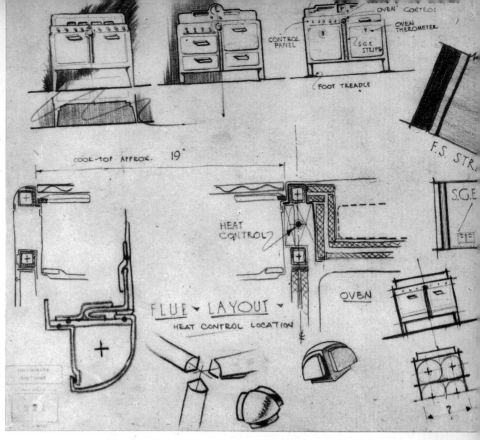

201 · PRELIMINARY SKETCHES FOR S.G.E. STOVES
DESIGNED BY NORMAN BEL GEDDES 1931

attempted to bring warped sheets into proper shape by tightening a bolt. Pressure applied to the sheet frequently produced a big fish-scale spall, or a series of radiating cracks.

Once the stove, having escaped injury during assembly, was erected, and crated for shipment, it still was subject to spoilage, owing to the brittleness of the enamel. If dropped while in transit, it sustained a concentration of stress at bolt holes; cracks and spalling were the results.

Extensive losses of this kind, due to conditions indicated, put upon the designer the necessity of evolving a design that would be less susceptible to these particular accidents. In other words, a way had to be found to relieve

202 · FINAL SKETCHES FOR S.G.E. STOVES   DESIGNED BY NORMAN BEL GEDDES 1932

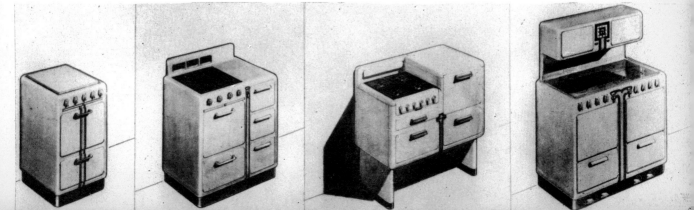

enameled sheet steel from the possibility of shocks, warpage and twists. This precluded the use of the finishing material, the outer shell, for structural purposes; since if an enameled piece is used as part of the structure the chances of its being damaged by stress in assembling or by shocks are greatly increased.

The solution of the problem was found in applying the principle of skyscraper construction. The skyscraper has a steel frame on which the walls and floors are built. The enormous weight of the masonry added as a skin is not carried clear to the ground through itself, but is transmitted to the steel frame. Similar methods are used in the construction of this stove. The skin, or enameled exterior, as well as the interior components of the stove, are attached to an independent steel frame.[203] If, in shipping, the stove is dropped, the frame takes the shock. The only shock sustained by the enameled sheet is

203 · S.G.E. GAS STOVE: WORKING DRAWING   DESIGNED BY NORMAN BEL GEDDES 1932

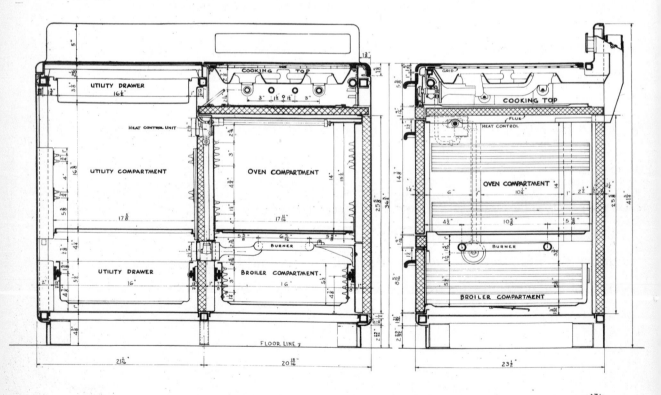

NORMAN BEL GEDDES
DESIGNER · NEW YORK

STANDARD GAS EQUIPMENT CORPORATION
FILE 221·02 NUMBER

DRAWING 104

VERTICAL SECTIONS
SCALE: 3 INCH EQUALS 1 FOOT
DRAWN   / /   TRACED   / /   CHECKED   / /

that due to its own weight. All exterior enameled parts are connected to the frame by means of hooked clips so arranged that they may be drawn up tight in assembly without subjecting the enamel to strain.

The former method — the bolt method — of assembly required much hand work, was time-wasting and expensive, requiring the insertion and tightening of many bolts and screws. By the skyscraper type of construction and the use of welding, the necessity for a hundred screws and bolts and the danger of spalling has been eliminated.

Superior in design, appearance and appointments, this stove is manufactured to sell at the price of an ordinary range, though it excels stoves now selling at a price well above it. A plain out-and-out cooking machine with no trick features, no gadgets, no decoration to dress it up. It does all that any

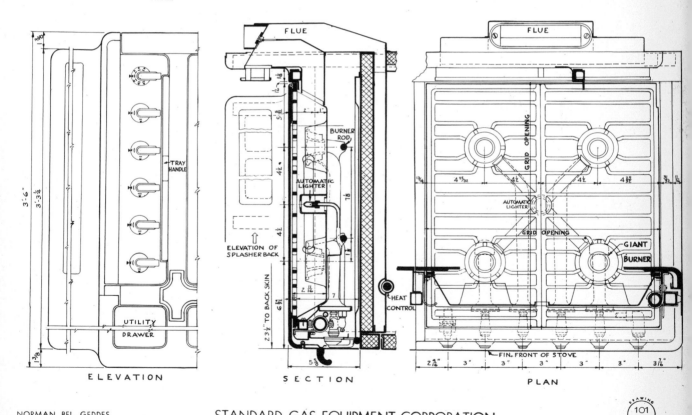

ELEVATION   SECTION   PLAN

NORMAN BEL GEDDES
DESIGNER · NEW YORK

STANDARD GAS EQUIPMENT CORPORATION

FILE
221·02
NUMBER

DRAWING
101
COOK TOP
SCALE: 3 INCH EQUALS 1 FOOT
DRAWN / / TRACED / / CHECKED

other stove will do as simply and as well, and is the easiest stove to use and keep clean on the market to-day. Its style in appearance is due entirely to its proportion and color. It is a good example of the coördination of mechanical engineering and visual design producing the desired result. As in any undertaking for a client, the confidence and whole hearted support of that client and the complete coöperation of his organization, is essential to the result. In this case the man who gave us his untiring support is W. Frank Roberts, President of the Standard Gas Equipment Corporation, manufacturers of a full line of stoves based upon this design.

CHAPTER 13

In Window Display the Play's the Thing

Too many display windows are cluttered with accessory paraphernalia when they are not overloaded with merchandise. That window is a failure which does not do three things in succession: arrest the glance; focus attention upon the merchandise; persuade the onlooker to desire it. The store window is a stage on which the merchandise is presented as the actors. The rules that apply to designing for the stage are in many ways true here. Keep the emphasis on the actor, for it is he who tells the story. This is the principle applied for the two years that I designed the merchandise displays in the windows of the Fifth Avenue department store of Franklin-Simon.

Such treatment presumes, first of all, a definite choice from among many systems that are possible in the light of display principles. It is necessary to define one clear line and adhere to it. The essential feature of any such method is that it shall include nothing which serves only as decoration.[208]

Many windows were designed with backgrounds conspicuous for their elaborateness.[205] Some stores adopted various ways of getting away from the window dressers' paraphernalia and introducing a more contemporaneous feeling into their windows but were afraid to go at the problem whole-heart-edly. They would set a piece of contemporary furniture in the window as a "fixture", with merchandise placed around and on it. Such a confessed make-shift was an individual window dresser's dash up an alley to escape from wearisome monotony. Affording no intrinsic beauty, force or selling power, such displays failed in any serious attempt to solve the problem of giving store windows a fresh point of view and interest in keeping with the merchandise, the times, and the prospective purchaser.[206]

Five years ago the most generally used window background was a highly varnished paneling of yellow oak. It is a color and finish that conflicts in a jarring way with almost any other color that can be put in front of it.[206] The next most common background in use was an imitation stone, as cheerless and uninviting as a mausoleum.[205]

In contrast with these, I designed a background, the chief value of which was its unobtrusiveness in form and color. The structure, built of wood, was plain except that at varying intervals in a horizontal direction a wave pattern rippled across it in relief.[212] The quiet beige of the walls was matched by a

205 · FRANKLIN SIMON WINDOW: PERFUME   DESIGNED BY FRED DOSCHER 1927

carpet and ceiling of the same color. Its high key gave a sense of gayety and life. In front of this the values of any other color stood out vividly but harmoniously. The six large windows became a compelling unit to every passer-by. As an ensemble they were sufficiently strong so that in several instances when using only the minimum of merchandise they achieved their most conspicuous success.

One display, consisting of just three articles of merchandise, had the most unexpected result.[207] An aluminum bust, wearing an Agnès turban, a scarf of vermilion and chartreuse green, occupied the center of the stage. A handbag in colors to match lay on a circular glass platform which supported the bust. The background was composed of large triangular shapes so composed as to focus attention on the *actor*. Hidden spotlights threw a blue shadow of the bust against this background. It was simple and unexpected. Shoppers looked and stopped. Observers from the other side of the Avenue crossed over, only to discover that the center of attraction was an almost empty store window. On one occasion the crowd swelled to such proportions that police

206 SAKS & COMPANY WINDOW   DESIGNER UNKNOWN 1925

Brown Brothers

reserves had to be called out to clear the way. Naturally, we felt that the effect of this display was in the nature of a " fluke." Some time later we used the same design again; the result was the same.

To begin with, in the Franklin-Simon windows, I endeavored to keep the color schemes within the laws of optics. Starting at the floor with a pale beige carpet, the walls, which matched the color of the carpet at the base, gradually· became darker as they approached the ceiling, the ceiling itself being a dark gray. The darkened ceiling dropped downward and the impression of a lofty, empty void disappeared. The result was a window neutral in character, rich in atmospheric tone, and fitted to serve as the embrasure for every variety of temporary, changeable background.[212]

Working in conjunction with this fixed background were four classifica-

Vandamm Studio

tions of interchangeable units, all of different materials. They were constructed so as to be set up in front of the window's permanent back and varied according to the merchandise displayed. Each of the four classes of units was developed in a radically different way as to form, material and color. To illustrate: Materials were classified in four groups - woods, metals, glass and textiles. Every material can be finished in a variety of ways, to bring out its most effective qualities. Metal panels can be made in sets of aluminum, blue steel, copper and brass. Wood panels may comprise unvarnished ebony and walnut as well as enameled surfaces in ultramarine, vermilion, and emerald green. Glass sets, wired for illumination from within, can be made of frosted, etched, stained, painted, mirror, and clear glass. Textile panels have a gamut to run — velvets, satins, silks, swansdown, leathers, even paper.

208 · FRANKLIN SIMON WINDOW: SHOES   DESIGNED BY NORMAN BEL GEDDES 1929

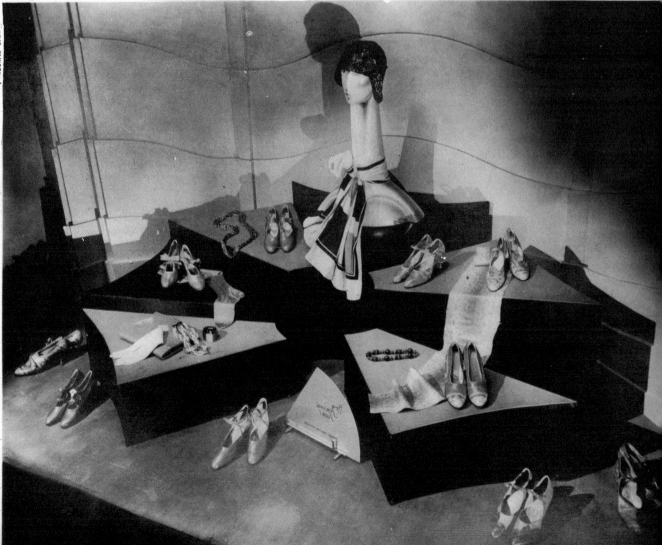

Vandamm Studio

It was found feasible to construct all panels in such a way that their component sections could be removed and interchanged with other panels. The same construction permitted open spaces affording a view of objects behind and beyond the panel surface. One of the major features of my method required the reduction of every accessory to a system of units. These units were interchangeable and at the same time furnished an endless variety of forms, all adapted to display purposes. With two units, four different combinations were possible; with three, nine; and so on in geometrical progression. The application of this unit system was somewhat like giving a turn to a kaleidoscope. The bits of colored glass fell into fresh geometric patterns with every fraction of a revolution.

As to length, breadth and height, the forms were all standardized to a unit dimension of four inches, or its multiple. The choice of four inches as the measurement unit was not arbitrary. It was selected after a careful study of store-window dimensions, merchandise peculiarities and other requirements. The four-inch unit appeared to be the minimum available for fitting in one piece with another and also for the employment of discrepancies in elevations which, operating on a difference of less than four inches, might appear to be accidental instead of intentional.

Taking these component pieces in their simplest form, the triangle, one can readily see how they adapted themselves to an enormous variety of sets or combinations.[207] Side by side, they provided a plain surface of any desired contour, elevated above the window floor. Placed one upon another, they gave a pyramidal structure of diminishing, receding angles. On end, they afforded screen effects. In combination, their possibilities and variety multiplied. Every unit was susceptible to instant transformation into the semblance of a fresh setting and this process of transformation could go on endlessly. Furthermore, the method automatically carried a definite style through the entire system of units, and in general gave the windows of this particular store individuality and distinction.

As an illustration of the unit system in actual practice, I refer to the shoe window of six units arranged asymmetrically.[208] Upon the highest unit an abstract bust wearing a lustrous straw hat and gay-colored scarf furnished the focal point for the composition. The various heights of the platforms made possible a shoe arrangement that permitted critical examination of each pair of shoes from any angle outside the window. The symmetrical character of the units themselves held the composition together and forced to the fore the merchandise. The accessories, the platforms, sank unobtrusively into their proper place while the merchandise dominated the scene. It was the old principle of the stage, wherein the setting was designed to throw the actors into relief.

Every unit piece, as constructed, was card-indexed for its several attributes.[209] The card recorded the individual number of the piece, its form, its material, the positions covered, the nature of the covering, the color of top, sides and bottom. On the reverse of the card appeared a diagram of the plan, elevation, dimensions and cross section. Every window set and every component part of every set was card-indexed in every detail, with the resources of the store's display department continually increasing in number and variety and with every item among those resources built up, from its inception, with the idea in mind of permanent availability. The store that put this plan into practice acquired a wealth of display material in the form of these units for a minimum cost.

Before constructing a single unit, I standardized the colors for the whole display system as definitely as was done with the forms of the units. First, I

209 · FRANKLIN SIMON WINDOW: CARD FILING SYSTEM   DESIGNED BY NORMAN BEL GEDDES 1928

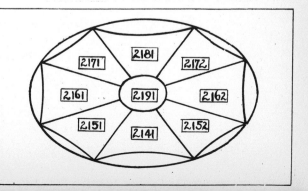

selected twelve variants of each of the three primary colors, yellow, blue, and red. In the scale of yellow, the range ran from lemon through cadmium and orange into brown; in the range of blues, from a purple-ultramarine through pure blue such as cobalt, to a green-blue on the border of cerulean; in the red range, from crimson through the madders into the magentas. Each of these thirty-six colors was so mixed that it would combine harmoniously without variation with any of the others. Units which were one color on the top and two sides were another color on the bottom and other sides. Consequently, by merely turning them over, we got a distinctly different color result. This more than doubled the utility of the pieces.

Once these colors existed in pigment, the next step was to duplicate each in the selected materials and textures. Each color was duplicated exactly in a soft matt finish, water-color texture, in a hard lacquered finish, in velvet, in silk, in felt, in leather, in wood, and in glass. To these were added certain metals, such as aluminum, copper, steel, and chromium plate. Six sets of samples the size of card-index cards were made up, and given a file number. They represented the key-set for all future color combinations. Whatever scientific formula was necessary to duplicate the sample was printed on the back of each. This method with regard to color created vast possibilities for combination and variety; and the flexibility of the unit form was increased rather than restricted by the use of color.

Color contrast and color harmony were used to accentuate the merchandise displayed. For instance, in the shoe window[208] the six units were covered in shiny antique satin, the top plane alone being a rich dark red. Monotony was avoided by having only four of the units placed with the red surface up. Against this red, the intricate pattern and strong color contrast of the reptile shoes appeared to advantage; whereas, the more subtle beige shoes stood out better against the black satin. The ivory mannequin, with her black straw hat and red, white and blue scarf, further accentuated and carried out the entire scheme. It may be interesting to note that this ivory mannequin[208] is a duplicate, except for color, of the aluminum mannequin in the single hat window.[207]

In a travel window the brilliant colors of the travel posters called attention to the tweed coat and matched pigskin bags of various sizes. Color was also used to suggest seasons, thus adding a touch of human interest. Eleven units made of chromium-plated tubes and glass plates combined into an abstract Christmas tree.[210] The base and branches were shelves for Worth's famous "Dans la Nuit" perfume.[211] Illuminated from the front with a pale red light, with three brilliant green shadows on the wall, the festive holiday spirit was complete.

210 · FRANKLIN SIMON WINDOW: PERFUME   DESIGNED BY NORMAN BEL GEDDES 1929

Vandamm Studio

In lighting the windows, the most modern methods known to the stage were applied. Stage lighting to-day involves the use of special lenses for lamps in the similar sense that a camera does in photography. The reason for this is found in the flexible nature of the spot-light beam. Non-focus or flood lamps in the form of footlights or arched strip lights cannot be concentrated upon a definite place where emphasis is needed. Lenses can do this. When an important bit of action is to take place, it is possible through the use of spot lights to give emphasis to the scene by a greater concentration of light at that point on the stage. Unimportant backgrounds are proportionately subdued to emphasize the actor, and the values of the scene are intensified by the amount of attention-compelling light. "Spot light" is a general classification. A dozen different combinations of lenses can be used on a single lamp for as many different results but very few people even in the theater know it.

The conventional lighting apparatus of display windows was and is thoroughly naive. It floods all parts of the windows, the background receiving as much light as the merchandise.[205] With this equipment it is impossible to concentrate a greater amount of light in one area than in another, regardless of comparative importance. Therefore I installed a large number of thousand-watt focus lamps in each window, with a varying assortment of interchangeable lenses and attachments. Mounted on universally adjustable swivels, they were equipped with soft edge irises to eliminate the severe edges of the light areas when desired. Beams from the spot light directed attention to the merchandise with emphasis and variety.

The elimination of realistic wax figures was another self-imposed limitation. Only abstract ones of my own design were used, and these were not grotesque atrocities such as appeared in other windows later. A mannequin who did not display the merchandise to better advantage than it could be displayed without her was regarded as a detriment. Under no circumstances was

211 · FRANKLIN SIMON WINDOW: PERFUME (DETAIL) DESIGNED BY NORMAN BEL GEDDES 1929

she allowed to focus attention upon herself. Special mannequins were made of glass.[212] Illuminated from the inside, they were used to reveal the delicacy of lingerie.

Instead of the customary show cards of cardboard,[204] I used frosted glass with beveled edges[208] and various metals. These have since come into general use.

Throughout, my method of handling the work was quite different from the general practice. I retained and found eminently satisfactory the same window-trimming department that the store had always had. In my studio was a scale model of the store's Fifth Avenue front one story in height. Models were also made to the same scale of all of our units. Within a few hours' time after being advised of the requirements of the store for the coming week, the problem was studied and the units set up in the windows of the model. Once the arrangement was satisfactory, working drawings were made. These were blue-printed and several copies were sent to the window-trimming department of the store the next morning. The window-trimming department was responsible for getting out of the storage rooms the particular units specified on the drawings by serial numbers, and for installing them according to the specifications and dimensions on the plan. These diagrams covered all phases of the work, the units, the merchandise, and the lighting.

212 · FRANKLIN SIMON WINDOW: LINGERIE   DESIGNED BY NORMAN BEL GEDDES 1929

Vandamm Studio

One of my assistants, delegated for supervisory work, passed on all the windows before they were disclosed to the public. This method, in general, and the unit system in particular, reduced costs and made excellent workmanship possible.

The credit should go to Mr. George Simon who invited me to try my hand. It was the Franklin-Simon windows that inaugurated the modern simplified and abstract trend in window display in this country, and for six weeks no effect was evident on other stores. Then presto! Within two months the whole street changed. For three years Fifth Avenue windows became more and more exciting to look at — and the passerby looked. Recently there has been a reaction that is disappointing. The note of simplicity has dwindled. Windows have again become elaborate and fussy. Moreover, the workmanship of displays is shoddy. The psychological effect of this is bad on the store.

Window displays are an expensive item of overhead for every store, in view of the amount of space given to them and the cost of this space on the ground floor and adjacent to the street. To insure the best utilization of this space, there should be a display system of the utmost creative scope and flexibility, yet sufficiently standardized in practical terms to impose upon the store's window dresser scant need for introducing special pieces, at the same time combining into compositions of genuinely arresting appeal. Merchandise and background should always tie up intimately, as actors and scenery are an integral part of the successful play on the stage.

213 · BISON   PAINTING BY CROMAGNON MAN 50,000 B. C.

CHAPTER 14

Changing World

MANY of the great accomplishments in art have developed in a period of great spiritual unrest, not at all unlike the present. The struggle itself has usually resulted in the birth of new ideas, in the development of new materials and new methods, and in the beginning of an upward step in the progress of humanity. Some of the drawing and painting on the walls of caverns in the Pyrenees Mountains made by Cro-Magnon men at least fifty thousand years ago have never been excelled in design and draftsmanship.[1] They represent drawing and painting under the most difficult conditions. It is interesting to note that in style they are as *modern* as any drawings being made to-day. The technical struggle of the men in achieving that startling simplicity of thought and form must have been tremendous, and I believe that the directness of the result was brought about to a great extent by their difficulties.

It was during the period of greatest turmoil that the Greeks developed their column-and-beam construction system and their work achieved its maximum vigor and simplicity.[2] But time, life and thought never stand still.

214 · RHEIMS CATHEDRAL DESIGNER UNKNOWN 1212

Having carried their idea to its highest point of development by the elimination of everything not essential to the complete design, they proved themselves completely human. Relaxing after their struggle, having more time at their disposal, unable to leave well enough alone, they began to "refine" and elaborate their art. Its decline was simultaneous with the deterioration of Greek civilization.

With equal intelligence, greater resources, plus all the experience of the Greeks and Etruscans, the Romans never succeeded in equalling in quality what had gone before. Although the Romans adopted the column and beam of the Greeks, and the arched vault and dome of the Etruscans, their greatest ability manifested itself in construction, and their chief contribution was the introduction of concrete.

Then, genius in architecture burst forth again in what we speak of as the Gothic.[214] A new combination of principles disclosed ways of creating new, inspiring forms. In combination with columns, they took sections of the walls and turned them at right angles to the wall line, forming buttresses, and they filled in the space between with great glass windows.[215] Color reached its most exalted expression in the thirteenth century through stained glass.

[274]

And now, hundreds of years later, we are at the beginning of another period that will rank with these others. But we are only *at* the beginning. One indication that this contemporary period is a beginning, and not a culmination, is to be found in the way we use steel. All the buildings built of steel to-day are mere preliminary models of the crudest sort by comparison with ultimate examples that will be achieved before the development of the steel structure reaches its maximum expression and starts downhill. We have but scratched the surface of the uses of this metal.

Many persons are under the impression that the progressive changes in design, commonly referred to as the modern style, which is so rapidly changing our environment for the better, is the result of an impetus that has developed within the past five years. This impetus has been under way for the past two generations. A graph-line would show its regular progress, with the single exception of the interval immediately

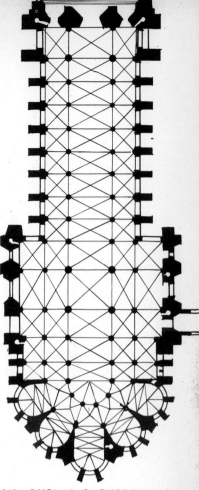

215 · RHEIMS CATHEDRAL: PLAN
DESIGNER UNKNOWN 1212

affected by the World War. Only now have the examples of this new expression accumulated in sufficient quantity to make themselves felt in various parts of the world. This is particularly true of the building media, architecture, sculpture, engineering.

This expression, the so-called modern style, was not the result of an attempt to be different nor was it a decorative movement. Serious people, whether they are artists or business men, do not think in such terms. It was a development that came as the result of fundamental thinking in terms of purpose, form and color.

For a very simple reason, this expression first manifested itself in painting, which for the last few hundred years has outsped the other arts. The differ-

216 · RHEIMS CATHEDRAL: ROSE WINDOW   DESIGNER UNKNOWN 1212

ence in cost between the materials required for experimenting with an idea on canvas and those required for the execution of an idea in the form of a building is considerable. The painter paints without commission. For him to test his experiment it is not necessary that he first have a contract signed and a client in the state of mind to spend thousands of dollars. The opposite is the case with the architect, sculptor, or engineer. The most that adventurous spirits can do in these fields is to visualize their ideas and develop them in the form of miniature models. There are all too few in a position even to carry their ideas that far, for again the cost involved is considerable.

Owing to the fact that one constantly hears design in its present-day aspect referred to as something of very recent origin, I have been curious to compare the earliest work I did in the theater with my latest work. My first designs for the stage (1913) and the photographs of my first production (1916) show clearly that, although cruder in execution than work I do today, it is just as direct and modern in its simplicity as anything I have done since. And there were others a long time ahead of me. Frank Lloyd Wright, for instance, has been working for forty years in terms of what is now spoken of as modern. He stands alone to-day as the most creative artist architecture has produced in America. During the World War, each of two neutral countries produced a young architect, both of whom, due to the head start they got during those several years wasted by the rest of the world, have had a major influence upon architecture immediately following the war. One was a young Swiss painter, Jean-

Aëronautical Chamber of Commerce

217 · LYCOMING AIRPLANE MOTOR   DESIGNED BY VAL CRONSTED 1929

neret, whom the world now knows as Le Corbusier. The other was J. J. P. Oud of Holland.

In support of my belief that all the common objects of our everyday life will continue to undergo vast changes as a result of the impetus toward design, facts of æsthetic and economic significance can be cited almost without limit. There is every indication that the mass of people have a deep-rooted craving for satisfaction from the appearance of the things around them. Year by year, the public judgment in such matters improves; and the reason is that the public is becoming more and more desirous of eliminating the uncouth. Take the automobile, as an example. The mass point of view for the selection of what might fairly be considered the best-looking motor car at the annual automobile show would be almost as dependable as the judgment of a care-

Margaret Bourke-White

fully chosen committee of three out of this mass. This situation arises from the fact that the motor car is a thing of our own generation. If the same public were shown examples of furniture of three hundred years ago, or sculpture, they would have much more trouble in arriving at a similar decision. In the latter case, they would be bothered about right and wrong, and beauty, and what other people think, and many other considerations all beside the point. But a still more important factor should be stressed. Regardless of their individual judgment in such matters, the desire and craving for objects of good design is increasing rapidly in the mass of the people. Already conscious of the tendency, they are becoming more and more sensitive to the elements of design in things about them. There are many proofs of this.

Not many years ago, practically all store fronts and store interiors followed one general style. In the hansom days, Fifth Avenue was decidedly this way. To-day it is different. Each store, large or small, endeavors to impress buyers with its individuality. They are aware of the consumers' increasing visual consciousness. Women are to-day buying four times as many pairs of shoes each year as their mothers bought at the same age. The shoes that the woman of to-day buys may not be so good as those her mother bought, but in her opinion they are smarter. She knows that if, instead of buying four pairs of shoes a year, she spent the same amount of money and bought one good pair, the one good pair would last more than a year. Also she knows that if she did this, she would look out-of-date, which is another way of saying that she is design conscious.

At the rate of more than ten million people daily, the American public throngs to moving-picture theaters. There they see people like themselves in surroundings with which, for the most part, they themselves are unfamiliar. They see how people in the other nine tenths of the world live. People in Kansas see how people not so unlike themselves live on Park Avenue, in London, in Tahiti. They see how these other people dress, what their dining rooms and their sleeping rooms are like, and they are influenced visually. They are becoming more design conscious. This same public reads popular magazines. These magazines are profusely illustrated, not only in the text, but in the advertisements concerning commodities in which the visual element is predominant. This again is profound proof of the public's interest in design. The same might be said of the latest ships launched by the French and North German Lloyd lines, which are, in their interior design, distinctly different in style from any ships previously built.

Furthermore, the satisfaction that arises from appreciation of good design is something that, once started, lasts forever. There is no end to it. If there were, persons who know a great deal about design would toss it aside as a boring matter having no further interest or value. The result is just the opposite. The more people know of this subject, the more interesting it becomes, the more it means to their daily life and the more they want to know. This is another reason why, year by year, the public's sensitiveness to design is increasing.

This craving to behold and to possess objects of good design is of course far more pronounced with a certain limited minority. Men with creative minds are exceedingly susceptible to the things around them. It is as natural for them to think of these objects in terms of improvements as for cream to rise to the surface of milk. For the artist, it is essential that he should be an explorer and delve into the future, both spiritually and materially; and if he works in the ideas and materials of his own age, he inevitably stamps his personality, sensitiveness, and ideas upon the world. The outstanding artists, many of whose names we do not know, but whose work defies time, are those who battered down the limitations of the then new materials and ideas of their time. It is so in terms of business men and it is so in terms of scientists, philosophers, writers and teachers.

Man has one outstanding failing — he limits his horizon to what his eyes see. He is too likely to be influenced in a transaction by the immediate consequences than to see it in perspective as a part of his life as a whole. He allows the obvious to offset his imagination. In the last five years the world has gone through a terrific change. Things are not the same as they were. To-day is no time for petty plans. The demand for leadership is dominant — whatever field you are thinking in. There are few limitations placed upon man other than those of his own making. It is up to him whether he broadens his viewpoint or

219 · DIRIGIBLE HANGAR, ORLY, FRANCE   DESIGNED BY H. FREYSSINET

not. His horizon is of his own making. Standing on the shore of the ocean and looking out to sea, his horizon is two and one half miles away. Leaning on the rail of the promenade deck of an ocean liner and looking out to sea, the horizon is eight miles away. If he climbs to the crows' nest, his horizon has increased more than six times what it was when he stood on shore.

Now is the time, for the world is changing, and the fellows on top when the smoke clears, will be those who changed with it. The specific phase of this change that I am speaking of in this book is with regard to visual design. The extent of these changes, which are bound to occur as the expression achieves fuller development, are only now beginning to be apparent. It is my expectation that better design will show first and most conspicuously in the common objects of domestic life, in such things as furniture, stoves, furnaces, lamps, refrigerators and telephones; and second in transportation conveyances, airplanes, motor cars, railway trains, and ships.

I anticipate that railroad, steamship and motor-car companies will not long continue to follow the design precedents they have followed in the past because they now realize that it is easy to improve their conveyances from the point of view of comfort and appearance and make them far more inviting to the traveling public. Eventually, these companies will employ only the best designers to solve the problems involving visual appearance, and for a very obvious reason. A good man who *solves* the problem is an economy in the long run, no matter what the original cost. He is a parallel to the lawyer who *wins* his case and the surgeon who *saves* a life. There is no middle ground.

Changes in household and office furniture will come more slowly than changes in automobiles. There are two fundamental reasons why it is easier to accept a marked change in the design of an automobile than a similar change in the design of furniture. First, we are naturally averse to change in objects that are part of our daily living habits; second, in purchasing furniture we usually add to what we have and consequently seek to buy something to go with it. As regards the automobile, our habits of thought are not so fixed as they are with regard to furniture. When we change cars, it is a matter of replacement at one stroke, and when we buy a new one we naturally select one that we believe to be better looking than the old one.

As to the form that motor buses will eventually take, I believe it will be that described elsewhere in these pages. My expectation is that buses of this form will be in general use on long runs in the very near future. Desirable changes in railway cars will come more slowly, since really effective changes will require the railroads and builders to discard present equipment. In the case of steamships, the process will require still longer. Nothing changes more slowly than ships of the sea.

Momentous changes in architecture are immediately ahead, particularly in domestic architecture. The house as we know it to-day is obsolete. In industrial architecture, the visual attractiveness of nearly every office building and factory has been achieved in a purely artificial manner. Where good design exists, it has come about mainly through attention to other things than the organic development of the basic form. Some of the most striking examples of architecture designed in this age are the grain elevators in the northwest.[218] Some may say this is not architecture. However, they are among the most honest examples of architectural design that have been originated since the pyramids. The Great Pyramid of Egypt is not only the world's most famous tomb, it is also one of the finest examples in architecture of designing to a purpose. Embodying the most intricate ideas, it succeeds in expressing them in the simplest of visual forms. In new forms, such as the pyramids were in their day, and as the grain elevators are in ours, it is easiest to break away from tradition and design organically. An outstanding example of designing for and in the spirit of our times are the twin dirigible hangars at Orly, France.[219]

The most fascinating change that is coming over the world to-day is the result of man's struggle to realize his vision of more congenial living conditions. In consequence of this vision and this struggle, many new developments are to be anticipated. The progress of the world from the earliest times up to the present has been towards the broader understanding of human welfare and relationship. In this connection consider the changing status of city planning. The scientifically designed mass-production house that can be fabricated in a factory, shipped anywhere and erected with all its facilities of lighting, heating, plumbing is yet to be realized. Present strides indicate that the solution is not far off.

There is said to be a law of nature that higher forms must, before maturity, pass through all the stages of evolution of their predecessors. This seems to hold true for the modern art of building. Mankind has had to re-experience the architectural development of the Egyptians,[1] the Greeks,[2] through the Gothic,[214] the Renaissance[161] and the Baroque, before it could express its own time in its own terms. Engineers and architects now seek to free city-planning conceptions from past influences, approaching the problem of municipal development from the viewpoint of its major considerations: first, problems involved in economies of space, material and labor; second, problems of intercourse and transportation; third, problems of public service, water, gas and electric supply, of sewage, and of labor-saving devices; fourth, problems of air and sunlight, of larger windows and of park areas; fifth, problems of housing the laboring forces of great industries.

Architects of the nineteenth century did not concern themselves with organizing the city as a center of production, but mainly with the development of residential quarters. They had their city halls, churches, banks, and museums and these were located wherever it was thought that they looked best. Wherever there was a plot of ground that was too small for a building, a monument was erected.[3] Washington and Paris are good examples of this sort of planning. But this is not the kind of planning that we are going to see in the future. As impractical as it may sound at the moment, cities of the future will be laid out and planned as a new industrial plant is — to achieve the utmost utility from all standpoints of the city problem.

Municipal governments will not eternally consist of and be ruled by politicians. We shall awake to the fact that our present political system is medieval and more out-moded than anything else we have. Municipal organizations of the future are going to govern for the benefit of the municipality, its living and its business. The most capable people in the municipality will run it in the same way that the best brains in a business manage it. Imagine the success that a large manufacturing plant would have if it were operated by a popular vote of all the people working in the plant? To-morrow, municipal governments embodying the brains of the community will plan their cities in the light of the city's needs.

By looking into the future and using a little imagination, vision and courage, we can attain results that will mean untold savings for future generations. The intelligent plan will be based upon the extreme of ultimate possible developments a good many years ahead. Then, by stepping the plan back in stages, we will reach the attainable objective for yearly periods. Nearly every large city has its plan for to-morrow, but these plans are of the vaguest sort and are based too much upon present conditions. I am speaking of such plans as the regional plan of New York City.

To-day, we know that a modern municipality is not to be regarded merely as a consuming center, but chiefly as a producing center with industry and commerce as the vital forces of its life. We can understand what it really is and should be only if we understand its economic functions, its labor divisions, and its labor associations. To-morrow's city planning will not commence with the secondary matter of residential districts, but with the primary object of establishing the production of the locality and of utilizing these possibilities to the fullest extent. It will, of course, consider residential necessities as a part of the whole and this will throw new emphasis and a new light upon the use and value of the tall building. Most people, in thinking of New York, think of the tall building sectors,[76] while actually the tall buildings occupy a very small proportion of the total area.[220]

The great value of the tall building in a city is that it towers high, furnishes its inhabitants with more and better air, sunshine, and space than they could possibly get otherwise in an equally populated section. Let us assume that the average height of all the buildings covering one entire block in lower Manhattan is ten stories. It is considerably less than this. Take fifteen blocks as a unit, each being ten stories in height.[221] Concentrate the floor space of all the buildings in these fifteen blocks into one tower covering one block. Such a tower might be one hundred and fifty stories high.

Within this one structure, occupying one block, we would have the same capacity as all the ten-story buildings covering the fifteen blocks. As a result, fourteen blocks are released for use as open country, or park, or airport, and we have a superior organism as far as an intercommunicating business system is concerned. The business of fifteen blocks is concentrated in one block and intercommunicating by vertical and horizontal transit systems. Multiply this principle by three, and we span the width of Manhattan. The space between each building is greater in width than the width of Central Park.

Such a development as this, although simple in itself, is sufficiently differ-

Fairchild Aerial Surveys, Inc.

ent from present-day conditions to require considerable foresight and planning on the part of business and municipal authorities. Real estate operators would not be very happy and could hardly be expected to flourish under such conditions. The property owners of all fifteen blocks would pool their interests and receive their proportionate dividends from the single building, the rest of the space being opened up for non-building purposes.

If the Empire State Building, instead of covering merely a quarter of a block, covered the whole block, and went as much higher as necessary, it would accommodate all the people now working within the surrounding half dozen blocks and accommodate them more comfortably than they are accommodated at the present moment. It would release these half dozen blocks for use as parks. Such a building would have the population of a fair-sized

Aero Service

city and contain every element that such a city would need to function, — its own fire department, hospital and police department. Obviously, these would be mere sub-stations of the metropolitan force.

In a building of this size, new problems will naturally arise. Transit problems within the building will be different. To-day even in our largest buildings only vertical transportation is provided. In the buildings of the future, problems of horizontal transportation will have to be solved, possibly by means of moving sidewalks in the nature of escalators.

The public at large thinks of skyscraper architecture as applying only to large cities. There are many arguments for its application to the small town. All the merchants in a town of five thousand persons will some day pool their interests. Instead of putting up numerous little three-story and four-story buildings of their own, they will build *one* tower-type building in the center of the town. This tower will not need to be very high, yet it will make life much easier for the whole community. Mrs. Jones will find it more convenient for her shopping, especially in rainy, hot or cold weather. In rainy weather she will be dry from the time she enters the building until she completes her errands. In hot weather, the building will be cooled by conditioned air, and in cold weather, heated. She will not be going from one draft temperature to another and slipping on icy pavements. The doctor, the movie and the butcher will all be under one roof, along with the commercial and governmental activities of the town, including the theater and the mayor's office.

For a community such as Greenwich, Connecticut, for instance, there is a particular advantage in this plan. The one building, occupying at the most a block, would release several blocks of valuable land, now used for business purposes, to enhance the comfort and charm of the community.

The architectural concentration just described might be looked upon as a symbol of similar developments in all phases of life, except that the symbol, instead of preceding the other phases, will undoubtedly follow it. Industrial organization is gradually changing from the free competition of independent companies, which in the past has been considered the protection of the consumer, toward a unification of these independent companies coöperating with each other towards a common purpose. Just as the forty-eight States of the United States can accomplish more as a united group, so can business institutions do the same. In so doing, these business institutions become a monopoly and the problem that is yet to be worked out is how to safeguard the public's interest. By organizing on such a scale, the output would be controlled, the cost of competition would be eliminated, and the evils of fluctuation in industrial activity would be greatly reduced. The heart of the plan should be a self-adjusting, economic mechanism.

As we progress, we will combine, which means we will work with the other person's interest in mind. To-morrow, we will recognize that in many respects progress and combination are synonymous. Civilization is as much the product of coöperation as of individualism. Behind us are generations of rampant individualists; ahead, I believe, lies an era of rational coöperation.

Some forms of industry will organize in much larger units than we know to-day. This tendency has already appeared in connection with the attempt of the railroads to solve their present difficulties. At first, the railroads in any one section of the country, as in New England, for instance, will operate as a unit. Eventually, all the roads in every section will comprise a single organism, as they did during the War. Other industries will follow this example as the method proves more economical, profitable and stable.

One of the greatest experiments the world has ever known is now in progress in Soviet Russia. Here is a government that is trying to run its affairs like a business. They are treating each separate undertaking, industry, art, or whatever it is, as though each were a subsidiary of the holding company.

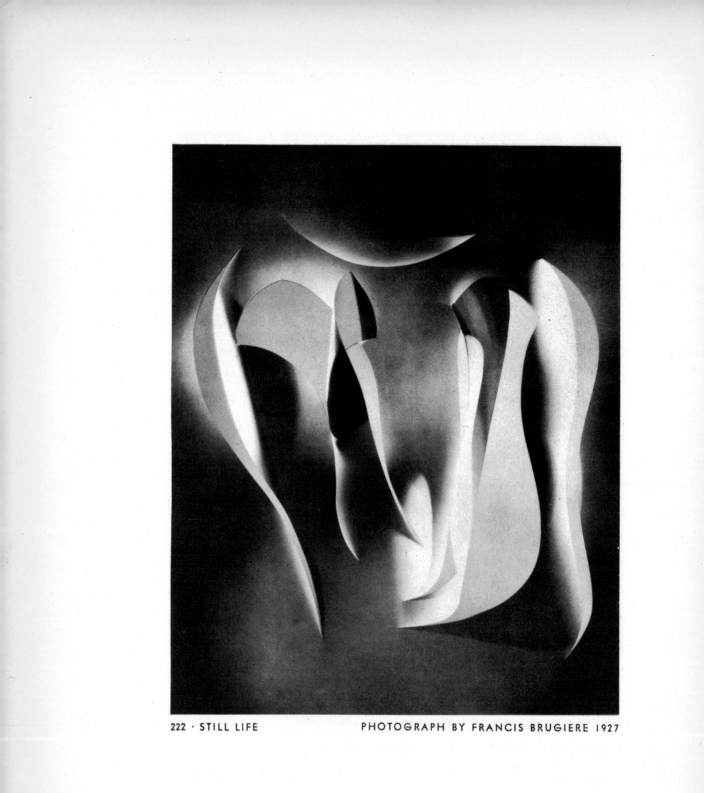

222 · STILL LIFE   PHOTOGRAPH BY FRANCIS BRUGIERE 1927

Each business is a single large combine, a great trust, if you wish to call it that, except that it is not run for purposes of personal or commercial profit for individuals. Of course unforeseen complications appear and great mistakes are made. This is the story of every experiment, large or small, and this is the largest the world has ever known. I am not expecting it to succeed in all phases, but I do foresee its success to an extent far beyond the present expectations of the American people.

The basic idea which differentiates the way the Russian Government undertakes to organize and operate its affairs from the way other governments try to run theirs is that they have a definite plan. They try at least to look ahead and see where they are going. A business that undertakes to operate on any other basis has little chance of success. A five-year plan that is only partially successful is better than a month to month plan or no plan at all.

In the United States, business is tending more and more towards organizing itself into larger units. What is happening in Russia is merely the maximum attempt, to date, of this tendency. Not so far in the future, the American people will be actively experimenting with further applications of a principle which originated on this side of the Atlantic. I refer to the principle of the huge industrial organism. One direct result of the new industrialized régime in the United States will be the inauguration of far-seeing plans for economies and efficiency in terms of future developments. Attention will be focussed upon the economic structure of the combine and its contribution to society. Directly and indirectly, this evolution will stimulate all the tendencies toward design that I have previously indicated.

Meanwhile, between various industries and between various enterprises within a given industry, there will be a more intensive rivalry to gain the confidence of the public for particular products. This will cause industry to concentrate upon quality as well as quantity of output, and it will bring into greater prominence than ever distinctions due to qualities of workmanship and design. The public will benefit. Their confidence and buying power will go to those industries which incorporate good design in their products, whether these industries sell things in packages, or, as in the case of railroads and motor-car makers, passenger miles.

This rivalry and competition for public favor, with concentration on quality as the first result, will have three other important and inevitable consequences. New materials and new methods will be developed to make the conditions of life more convenient, comfortable and agreeable. We shall acquire an adequate machine craftsmanship. As between industry and the artist, their common interests will be further consolidated.

Progressive business means new ideas, and new ideas invariably stimulate progress in design; progress in design brings technical progress. The three go hand in hand. Very little has been accomplished as yet in the constructive exploitation of new metals and alloys. We may anticipate that miracles will be performed by the chemist and metallurgist with rare metals such as tantalum and molybdenum. A new alloy, thin as paper, and impermeable to hydrogen and helium, will make possible the all-metal dirigible. Transportation by air will develop rapidly in the new era. The latest generation has been born to the air, as others of us have been born to the railroad, steamship and automobile. This new generation will live to see mass production airplanes in daily use by the thousands. These machines will be as easily handled as the automobile. New devices will make it possible to fly blind in all weather. Planes will be stamped out by mass production methods. Engines will be made largely of some light-weight alloy, such as beryllium. Probably, the engines will approximate the turbine principle. Television may be a commonplace within a decade. Art will be achieved by the machine – inspirationally and technically.

Artists are fast mastering the camera, which is purely a machine. The camera will develop into the perfect instrument for the artist. It automatically attends to the obvious and literal for him. It reacts instantly to his sensitiveness and creative imagination.[222] But it is a foreign tool to the artist. Not much technique has been developed for it as yet. The pencil or brush is a simple thing to master. The camera is intricate. The same applies to the artist in industry.

Of one thing we can be sure. All the industrial design we have had in the United States, as yet, is comparable in effect to a pebble dropped in a pond. The circles that have agitated the surface will continue to widen and spread with an ever-increasing sphere of influence. By the middle of the present century, I anticipate that we shall have begun consciously to achieve that complete mastery of the machine which is to-day a more or less unconscious goal. By that time, it will be one of the profoundest facts of our existence. It will make for our greater peace and contentment and yield not only purely physical but æsthetic and spiritual satisfaction.

But at the moment, we still are thinking too much in grooves. We are too much inclined to believe, because things have long been done a certain way, that *that* is the best way to do them. Following old grooves of thought is one method of playing safe. But it deprives one of initiative and takes too long. It sacrifices the value of the element of surprise. At times, the only thing to do is to cut loose and *do the unexpected!* It takes more even than imagination to be progressive. It takes vision and courage.